M000094771

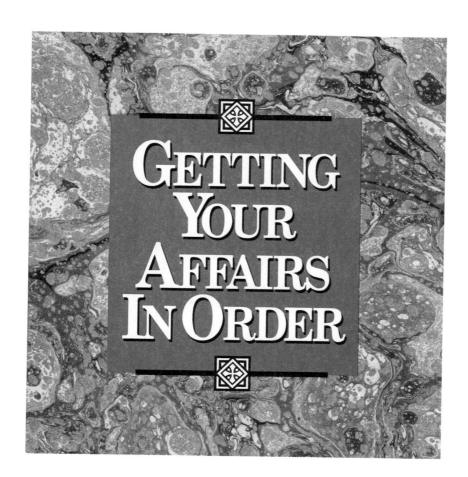

GETTING YOUR AFFAIRS IN ORDER

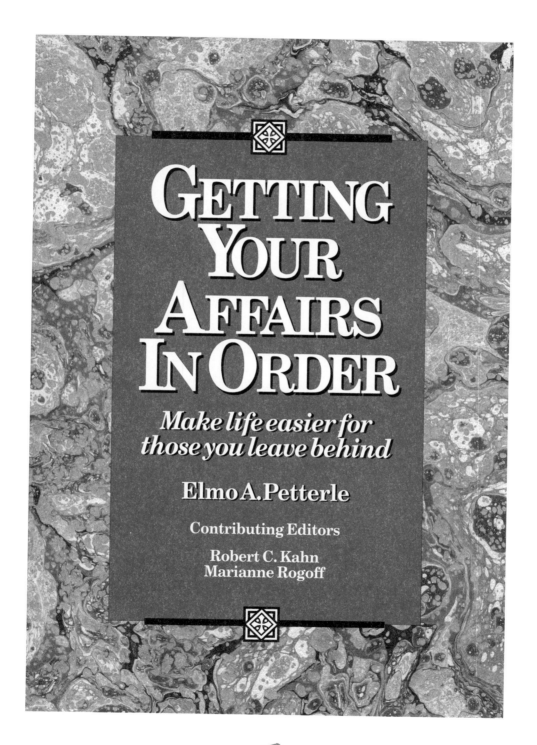

GETTING YOUR AFFAIRS IN ORDER

Make life easier for those you leave behind

Elmo A. Petterle

Contributing Editors

Robert C. Kahn
Marianne Rogoff

SHELTER PUBLICATIONS INC
Bolinas, California

Copyright © 1993 Elmo A. Petterle

All rights reserved. No part of this publication
may be reproduced or transmitted in any form or
by any means, electronic or mechanical, including
photocopy, recording, or any information storage
and retrieval system without the written
permission of the publisher.

Distributed in the United States and Canada by:
Ten Speed Press
PO Box 7123
Berkeley CA 94707

LIBRARY OF CONGRESS
CATALOGING-IN-PUBLICATION DATA

Petterle, Elmo A., 1914 –
    Getting Your Affairs In Order/Elmo A. Petterle;
contributing editors, Robert C. Kahn, Marianne Rogoff.
        pp. 117   cm. 8 1/2 x 11
    Rev. and simplified ed. of: Legacy of Love. © 1986
    Includes bibliographical references and index.
    ISBN 0-936070-15-3 (Shelter)
    ISBN 0-89815-547-9 (Ten Speed)
    1. Estate planning—United States—Popular Works.
I. Kahn, Robert C. II. Rogoff, Marianne.
    III. Petterle, Elmo A., 1914 –
Legacy of Love. IV. Title.
KF750.Z9P475 1993
346.7305'2—dc20   93 – 21882
[347.30652]   CIP

2 3 4 5 — 97 96 95 94
Lowest numbers indicate number and year of this printing.

First printing: June 1993

Printed in the United States of America

Additional copies of this book may be purchased
for $12.95 plus $3 shipping and handling from:

    Shelter Publications
    PO Box 279
    Bolinas CA 94924

Or write for free catalog of books.

We are grateful to the following publishers and
authors for permission to reprint portions of
previously published material:

Celo Press, Burnsville, NC, for sample death ceremony
on page 20 from *A Manual of Death Education and
Simple Burial* by Ernest Morgan. © 1984. Reprinted by
permission.

Doubleday & Company, Inc., Garden City, NY, for stories
appearing on pages 45 and 81, from *Everything Yours
Heirs Need to Know About You* by David S. Magee. ©
1981, 1983 by David S. Magee. Reprinted by permission.

The New York *Times,* New York, NY, for excerpt on
page 84, from "Where There's a Will" by William D.
Zabel, originally appearing May 20, 1984.
© 1984. Reprinted by permission.

Stephen Jamison, Ph.D., for pages 99–100,
Understanding Grief and Loss. Reprinted by
permission of the author.

ACKNOWLEDGMENTS

MY SINCERE thanks and continued love to my wife, Kay, for her patience and understanding during the many months it took to develop the material to write this book.

A particular vote of thanks to my children — Carol Carpenter, Joe Petterle, and Steve Petterle — for their input, suggestions and encouragement, without which this book could not have been written.

Finally, special thanks to my wonderful grandchildren — Lynn, Bart, Marc, Joey, Sarah, Matt, Katie and Alexis — for giving me the inspiration to leave a legacy of love.

PUBLISHER'S NOTE

THIS BOOK is a revised and simplified version of Elmo Petterle's original book *Legacy of Love*, published in 1986. Since then, the public perception of death and its variety of forms has matured substantially. Death is more spoken of these days. People have begun to think more realistically about it. Why? For a variety of reasons: Derek Humphry's book *Final Exit*, with specific instructions on ending one's own life, became a bestseller; Dr. Jack Kevorkian, who has assisted terminally ill patients to die, has generated nationwide publicity; and the continuing spread of AIDS and cancer — all of this has caused us to be a little more aware of something we all must face sooner or later: the natural, inevitable end to our lives.

Getting Your Affairs in Order is a workbook, a single place where you can document the many things that must be taken care of by your survivors after your death. It differs from the previous book in that it is more streamlined, more clearly organized, and therefore easier to fill out. But the general idea is the same: if you take the time to pre-plan now, and fill out any of this book, you will be leaving a thoughtful, wonderful legacy for your survivors.

CONTENTS

I expect to pass through this world but once;
any good thing therefore that I can do,
or any kindness that I can show to any fellow creature,
let me do it now;
let me not defer or neglect it,
for I shall not pass this way again.

—Stephen Grellet
(Etienne de Grellet du Mabilier)

INTRODUCTION

GETTING YOUR AFFAIRS IN ORDER is designed for the use of everyone — young or not so young, healthy or not so healthy, rich or not so rich — men, women, married or single. It is for anyone who has compassion, who cares enough to make life easier for the ones they will someday leave behind.

Studies reveal that over 90% of survivors are unprepared to handle the many immediate and future responsibilities that arise when a death occurs. Why? Simply because no one likes to think or talk about, much less deal with, death. Consequently, few people plan for it.

The purpose of this book is to take death out of the closet and deal with its realities. This may not be easy to do. Some of the tasks outlined in the following pages may seem harsh or difficult if you have never considered your own mortality. However, it is highly important to fill these pages out. Be positive. Remember: if you don't do it now, it will have to be done later by a loved one, under much less favorable conditions.

The many details surrounding death — burial arrangements, financial and legal matters, notification requirements, miscellaneous paperwork and such — come at a time of great stress for survivors. Though many of these tasks are not hard, some are time-consuming and can be quite costly when research and legal services are required. Most of the decisions that need to be made at the time of death or shortly thereafter can be made in advance while your thinking is clear. Information can be easily obtained and sorted, and alternatives can be researched, thoroughly reviewed, and discussed.

Getting Your Affairs in Order will show you, step by step, what can be done before a death and what must be done by survivors later. Most of the information and forms here are easy to complete. Some will require research and gathering of information, either by phone, mail or in person. All, however, will be much easier to complete and take less time before, rather than after, a death.

Once your affairs are in order, you will be able to store the information, forget it and celebrate your accomplishment by enjoying life to the fullest each day.

–Elmo A. Petterle

TO THE BENEFACTOR

Benefactor: one who renders aid or kindly service; a friendly helper

WE ALL TEND TO THINK we are immortal, or too young to worry about death; we avoid thinking or talking about it, or even saying the word. But, having purchased this book and read this far, I'll assume you are in a frame of mind to accept the fact that death is a part of life — for everyone. And now is the time to treat it as sensibly as you would any other important matter that requires serious thought and advance planning.

Getting Your Affairs in Order is a strategic planning tool for all ages, a workbook to be filled in by you that will make life easier for your eventual survivors. The book lists over 60 responsibilities that your survivors will have to face. You can take care of many of these in advance. Step by step, in order of importance, you will be able to pre-plan and document vital survivor information, no matter how far in the future your loved ones will use and appreciate your thoughtfulness.

What's in it for you if you complete this task?

■ First, there is immediate practical use in the month-to-month management of your existing finances and assets.

■ Next, while you are here, you can see that the legacy you leave will be free of serious problems.

■ Finally, you will enjoy the satisfaction that comes from getting your affairs in order.

It's been said that nothing is certain in this life except death and taxes. Every year most of us plan ahead and seek help to take care of our taxes. Just this one year, why not take time to plan for life's other certainty? Peace of mind and untold benefits are guaranteed for you and your survivors if you do so.

*You can never
do a kindness
too soon
because
you never know
how soon
it will be
too late.*

—Emerson

TO THE SURVIVOR

To be read immediately after a death

A THOUGHTFUL, CARING PERSON wanted to make life easier for you at this difficult time. Recognizing that all this would be hard for you, this outline of what must now be done has been left behind — the what, where, when and how of your responsibilities following a death.

After calling your family and friends, turn to the *Who-to-Contact Directory* on page 10, where you will find a list of immediate after-death contacts and phone numbers, in order of importance. This previously documented information will speed up arrangements which must now be made and help eliminate unnecessary delays in benefits to which you are entitled. Timely action will help clear up your estate quickly and keep your financial affairs running smoothly so you can go on with your life.

There is much to be done, starting within hours after death. Don't try to do it all yourself. The pain of your loss and handling the immediate details are all you need to consider in the first week or two. Take time before thinking about managing the many tasks that can wait. Don't be afraid to ask family and friends for help. Believe it or not, they will be flattered. Many people want to help, but feel awkward about offering assistance. Delegate specific tasks whenever possible.

There is no easy way to escape the sorrow that accompanies a loved one's death nor to escape the necessity of mourning. In addition to grief and sorrow, you may be feeling fear, guilt, anger or other unanticipated emotions; this is perfectly normal. Let your feelings run their course. During this period, hold off on making permanent decisions. Consult with professionals when necessary.

Use this book. And take it to heart that someone cared enough to leave it for you.

HOW TO START

THIS BOOK HAS been designed with several users in mind — the benefactor, a thoughtful and caring person who wants to make life easier for those left behind, and the survivors who have to carry on in the absence of that person.

PROCEED STEP BY STEP

■ **SKIM THE BOOK** Get a general overview, then take a closer look at what's involved. I have outlined my recommended order of priorities in the *Who-to-Contact Directory* on page 10, but you may determine your own priorities depending on your situation and needs.

■ **START WITH A PENCIL** Write down everything you can from memory. Using a pencil will allow you to erase and update periodically. You will be surprised at the amount of important information (not generally known by others) that you know off the top of your head.

■ **PREPARE A WILL** No one has ever seen a hearse in a funeral procession towing a trailer — you can't take it with you! However, you can take peace of mind with you, knowing that what you have worked so hard to acquire will be distributed in accord with your wishes, as outlined in your will.

IF YOU DON'T HAVE A WILL, your first priority is to get one prepared.

IF YOU DO HAVE A WILL, review it to see if any changes should be made.

THIS POINT CANNOT BE STRESSED TOO STRONGLY!

See page 84 for more information on will preparation.

■ **COMPLETE THE BOOK** As time permits, fill in all the forms, in priority as you see fit. If you need to make contact with outside agencies, do so — and note your agreements on the appropriate forms. Locate documents (policies, contracts, etc.) and note where they are on the *Location of Records* form on page 14.

FILLING IN THE NAMES AND PHONE NUMBERS IN THE *WHO-TO-CONTACT DIRECTORY* IS THE SINGLE MOST IMPORTANT TASK IN THE BOOK.

If you do nothing else, a well-completed directory will accomplish a great deal for your survivors; at least they will know who to contact for further information. *(See page 10).*

■ **DISCUSS THE CONTENTS WITH THOSE WHO SHOULD KNOW** Once the book is completed, sit down and go over it with those who will be using it later. Make sure they understand your wishes. Then find a safe place to store it — not a safe deposit box, as the book itself contains information on the location of your box and key. Also, you will need to update the book regularly. I suggest keeping it with your file of current bills and active documents and reviewing the work each year when you do your tax return.

■ **BE SURE YOUR LOVED ONES KNOW WHERE THIS BOOK IS KEPT.**

Every rewarding accomplishment has a beginning and an end, with much to be done in between. What follows is the serious beginning of your legacy.

Don't put it off. And good luck!

FIRST
THINGS
FIRST

PART I contains information which survivors will need in the first hours and weeks immediately following a death. Everything will be easier to handle for those left behind if the pages in this section are filled out.

Relatives, friends and business associates are the first people who should be called. Then the *Who-to-Contact Directory* outlines the next steps to take, in order of priority: arranging for disposition of the body, memorial services and obituaries, contacting lawyers, trustees, insurance companies and so on until everything is running smoothly once again.

Relatives, Friends, Business Associates

Include names of doctor, attorney, employer,
executor or trustee of estate and anyone else
who should be called immediately after a death.

Name	Phone #	Address

NAME	PHONE #	ADDRESS

WHO-TO-CONTACT DIRECTORY

Use this directory as a quick referral guide. It lists some of the many contacts survivors will have to make in the days immediately following a death, in order of priority and importance.

IMMEDIATE CONTACTS

Most of these contacts can be delegated and handled by phone.

ITEM	SEE PAGE	NAME & PHONE #	COMMENTS
RELATIVES AND CLOSE FRIENDS	8		A list of names and phone numbers appears on page 8.
FUNERAL HOME OR MEMORIAL SOCIETY	18		Advise of time of death, present location of deceased and your wishes regarding disposition and services.
CEMETERY OR FINAL RESTING PLACE	16		Coordinate with memorial services.
DEATH CERTIFICATES	18		Obtain from funeral home or county office of vital statistics.
EMPLOYER/BUSINESS ASSOCIATES	8		Call to inform of death.
PERSON TO GIVE EULOGY	8		Coordinate with person conducting services.
PALL BEARERS	8		Coordinate with cemetery and with person conducting services.
NEWSPAPER OBITUARY	21		You may wish to delegate this to others or the funeral director.
ATTORNEY	8		Your attorney should coordinate executor, trustee and estate matters for you.
EXECUTOR AND/OR TRUSTEE OF ESTATE	8		Contact to begin process.
OTHER IMMEDIATE CONTACTS	8		

Page numbers in the second column refer to completed forms in this book documenting benefactor's wishes, previously-made arrangements, and financial and other matters.

11

3–5 Day Contacts

Item	See Page	Name & Phone #	Comments
Life Insurance Agent	32		Report death and provide death certificates for early claim payment.
Military Pension & Veterans Organizations	40		May provide death benefits for veterans.
Labor, Trade, or Credit Union	8		May provide death benefits for members.
Fraternal Organizations	8		May provide death benefits for members.
Social Security	34		Call local office to continue benefits.
Medicare	35		Submit form "Payment for Services to Patient Now Deceased".
Supplemental Medical Insurance	38		Contact for balance payable after Medicare settles. Some policies provide death benefits.
Other 3–5 Day Contacts			

5–10 Day Contacts

Item	See Page	Name & Phone #	Comments
Insurance Agent	70		Notify to change name on policies. Some policies contain death benefits.
Bank(s) and S & L Institutions	44		Ask about name change requirements. (Probate may be necessary.)
Mortgage Co.	50		Some mortgage contracts include life insurance.
Property Mgr. or Landlord	48		If you own or rent property, notify of changes as appropriate.
Pension or Profit Sharing Plans	33		Phone for forms to be sent so you can obtain benefits.
IRA , Keogh Plans	33		Call accountant to obtain info on collecting IRA funds.
Money Market Accounts	46		Ask about name changes. (Probate may be necessary.)
Mutual Funds	46		Ask brokerage firm about name change requirements.
Stocks & Bonds	46		Ask brokerage firm about name change requirements.
Accountant/CPA	62		Alert that tax planning changes may be necessary.
Financial Counselor	62		Revision of financial plan may be necessary.
Mortgages, —We Owe	50		May be due on death.
Notes, Loans— We Owe	50		May be due on death.
Other 5–10 Day Contacts			

10–30 Day Contacts

Item	See Page	Name & Phone #	Comments
County Recorder			Titles may need to be changed. Ask attorney for advice as necessary.
Post Office			Notify of name change, as appropriate.
DMV	70		DMV has forms for name change.
Telephone	60		All can be notified of name change with next bills.
Gas & Electric	60		
Water Company	60		
Garbage Disposal	60		
Paper/Magazine Subscriptions	61		
Department Stores	61		
Credit Cards	15, 61		
Clubs/ Organizations	8		
Cable TV	61		
Other 10–30 Day Contacts			

LOCATION OF RECORDS

This form is VERY IMPORTANT! Whether you have these documents in a safe deposit box, locked file cabinet, shoe box, or scattered throughout the house, try to find them now and record their location in the appropriate space here.

ITEM	WHERE KEPT	COMMENTS	SEE PAGE
**WILL			
SAFE DEPOSIT BOX & KEY			45
BANK PASSBOOKS			44
*T-BILLS, CDs			44
MONEY AND MUTUAL FUNDS			46
PENSION, IRA, KEOGH INFO			33
SOCIAL SECURITY RECORDS			34
VETERANS			40
*INSURANCE POLICIES			32, 38 70
*DEEDS OF TRUST			48
*STOCKS AND BONDS			46
LOANS—OWED TO US *ORIGINAL PROMISSORY NOTE			52
LOANS—WE OWE			50
BUSINESS RECORDS & CONTRACTS			50, 52

* Recommend keeping in safe deposit box.
** If there are funeral instructions in the will, best to keep a copy of the will in accessible place. Or make funeral instructions known to someone. *See page 19.*

ITEM	WHERE KEPT	COMMENTS	SEE PAGE
LIMITED PARTNERSHIPS			46
REAL ESTATE RECORDS			48
*AUTO OWNERSHIP CERTIFICATES			70
CURRENT AND PAST INCOME TAX			62
CREDIT CARDS (PLUS ACCOUNT NUMBERS)			61
WARRANTIES			
*BIRTH CERTIFICATES			
PASSPORTS			
BURIAL CONTRACT			17
FUNERAL CONTRACT			19
OTHER			

CEMETERY OR FINAL RESTING PLACE

PERHAPS ONE OF THE TOUGHEST THINGS to think about is what you might want done with your body after you pass on. Once you decide, follow through. Look in your Yellow Pages under *Cemetery* or *Cremation* and contact the appropriate agency to make arrangements. This may seem difficult, but think of the state of mind of the person doing it later.

YOUR OPTIONS

■ **BURIAL** In the old days, Americans buried their dead in a family or church graveyard, but state laws now dictate that burial can take place only in licensed cemeteries. Cemetery lots can be purchased in advance for yourself and any number of family members. Prices will differ for urban and rural lots, hilltop sites or a spot on lower ground. A concrete vault might be offered to surround the coffin, preventing water seepage and settling of the soil, or entombment, where the body rests in a coffin in a tomb or crypt above ground, in a building called a mausoleum. You can purchase crypts for an individual or a whole family. Perpetual care is another price variable. Make phone calls and ask about alternatives and prices.

■ **CREMATION** In many parts of the world, cremation is the preferred method of taking care of the body after death. If cost is a factor, this is an inexpensive solution. Afterwards, the ashes are put in a box or urn and can be returned to the survivors for scattering, burial in a cemetery grave, or placement in a niche or vault in a columbarium (a special building to house these urns). Some religions oppose cremation, and others that have opposed it in the past now accept it, provided a document previously completed by the deceased is on record.

■ **DONATION OF BODY OR ORGANS** Much has been learned in the field of medical science by studying bodies which have been donated for this educational purpose. Medical schools will generally arrange for final disposition of the body, or you may request that cremated remains be returned to the survivor for burial or scattering. If you are serious about donating your body for study or your organs for possible transplant into live persons in need, contact the anatomy department at the medical school nearest you and make arrangements. *The Uniform Anatomical Gift Act* law is in effect in all 50 states, and allows you to document your desire to donate your body or organs. *See page 93 for more information.*

Once you have discussed all your options, have the agency provide you with a written agreement stating what you have decided, what the price includes, and how and when it is to be paid. If paid in full in advance, agree that there will be no additional charges, as the agency will have use of the money and interest accrued from time of payment until services are needed. Consider setting up a third-party trust or special bank account as an alternative to paying the agency directly.

When this is done, all that survivors will have to do later is make a telephone call. This will considerably reduce the burden on your family and loved ones at a difficult time.

A peace above all earthly dignities,
A still and quiet conscience.

–Shakespeare

BURIAL ARRANGEMENTS

NAME OF CEMETERY OR
OTHER RESTING PLACE _____

ADDRESS _____

_____

PHONE # _____

PERSON CONTACTED _____

DATE CONTACTED _____

The following arrangements have been made:
(burial, headstone, inscription, opening/closing grave,
crypt, donation of body, cremation, other).

_____

_____

_____

_____

| FINANCIAL AGREEMENTS | _____ | APPROXIMATE TOTAL COST | _____ |
| LOCATION OF CONTRACT | _____ | DATE PAID IN FULL | _____ |

SPECIAL WISHES _____

_____

_____

FUNERAL OR MEMORIAL SERVICE

SOON AFTER THE RESTING PLACE contact has been made, think about your funeral. Your religion may have guidelines for appropriate mourning and burial rituals. Most Americans still prefer the traditional elaborate services of a funeral home, though joining a "memorial society" and making arrangements through them is becoming more common. An unstructured, personal death ceremony which reflects the person's life is a fine alternative to a formal funeral. *(See page 20.)*

YOUR OPTIONS

■ **MEMORIAL SOCIETIES** exist throughout the country to assist survivors in making low-cost arrangements at the time of a death. Most recommend cremation followed by a simple memorial service which may include burial or scattering of ashes. For a fee (as low as $25), you can become a member and be sent forms to fill out, expressing your wishes. Check your Yellow Pages under *Funeral* or *Cremation Services*.

■ **FUNERAL HOMES** are full-service oriented. Like any business, all types of products and services will be available, at a variety of costs. They can arrange for delivery of the body from the place of death to the funeral home and resting place. You may rent a hearse and limousines for the funeral for a price. The coffin can be the most expensive part of your burial costs. From a simple pine box to polished carved mahogany with satin lining and pillow, the price can range from a few hundred to thousands of dollars. Embalming is another option, which preserves the looks of the body for an open viewing. It is not, however, required by law. As with your resting place arrangements, this can all be prepaid.

■ **MEMORIAL SERVICES** differ from a funeral in that the body of the deceased is not usually present. They are often held when family and friends cannot congregate immediately after a death, or it may simply be your wish to have this type of service rather than a funeral.

The location may be a funeral home, church, community center, your own home, a boat at sea, or some other special place. If the entire memorial is held at a funeral home, the cost is included in their bill. Where there is no charge for a church or other facility, a donation for its use, and individual donations for people involved in the service, is in order. You may want someone in particular to deliver a eulogy. Would you like music, food, readings, any special guests? Use the form provided here to make your wishes known.

DEATH CERTIFICATES

Certified copies of death certificates will be needed in order to file papers for insurance and other benefits. The survivor can get these from the funeral home (if you are using one) or county Office of Vital Statistics.

If not using a funeral home, a properly filled-out death certificate and a "Permit of Disposition" is required by law before burial can take place.

We are such stuff
As dreams are made on; and our little life
Is rounded with a sleep.
—Shakespeare

FUNERAL ARRANGEMENTS

NAME OF FUNERAL HOME
OR OTHER FACILITY _____

ADDRESS _____

_____

PHONE # _____

PERSON CONTACTED _____

DATE CONTACTED _____

The following arrangements have been made:
(delivery of body, type of coffin, embalming, church service or other
location, public or private, food, drink, music, readings).

_____

_____

_____

_____

OTHER FINANCIAL
AGREEMENTS _____

APPROXIMATE
TOTAL COST _____

LOCATION OF CONTRACT _____

DATE PAID
IN FULL _____

SPECIAL WISHES _____

_____

_____

AN UNSTRUCTURED SERVICE
HELD IN A FARMYARD

This was a service held for Tom. He had grown up
on a farm near a small city. He had lived in the
same community all his life. After he died, his
brother arranged for a memorial service held
outdoors in the farmyard, just as Tom once, years
before, had said he'd like it to be.

Chairs were carried out onto the lawn; a table of
soft drinks was set up at one side. A rowboat that
Tom had enjoyed using on the river was filled with
garden and field flowers; it also held a self-portrait
Tom had painted.

There were some prepared readings, but guests
were invited to, and did, speak as the spirit moved
them to do so about their love for Tom.

A Manual of Death Education and Simple Burial
                              –Ernest Morgan

Whatsoever things are true,
Whatsoever things are honest,
Whatsoever things are just,
Whatsoever things are pure, Whatsoever
things are lovely,
Whatsoever things are of good report:
If there be any virtue,
and if there be any praise,
Think on these things.
                              –Phillippians 4:8

OBITUARY

WHAT WOULD YOU LIKE your local newspaper to say about you when you have passed on? Look at obituaries in the newspaper; these generally summarize the chief accomplishments of a person's lifetime. You may wish it to be a full reflection of the richness of your life, something more short and simple, or somewhere in between. Either way, filling in this page will provide a good resumé to leave your heirs and could be useful in other areas as well.

Survivors may delegate this task to a friend if they wish, or if using a funeral home, they will normally take care of notifying the newspaper at the appropriate time.

NAME _____

DATE OF DEATH _____

CAUSE OF DEATH _____

DATE OF BIRTH _____

PLACE OF BIRTH _____

CURRENT RESIDENCE _____

CAREER BACKGROUND _____

_____

SPECIAL ACHIEVEMENTS _____

EDUCATION _____

_____

MILITARY SERVICE _____

CLUBS, UNION, OFFICES HELD _____

_____

RELIGION, POLITICS _____

ATHLETICS, HOBBIES _____

SURVIVORS _____

_____

_____

PLACE OF SERVICE _____

DATE AND TIME OF SERVICE _____

MEMORIAL CONTRIBUTIONS PREFERENCE _____

NAMES OF NEWSPAPER(S) _____

_____

SPECIAL NOTES OR COMMENTS _____

_____

TIPS FOR SURVIVORS

SAFE DEPOSIT BOX

A day or so after the services, or when the family feels up to it, survivors may want to inspect or remove the contents of the safe deposit box. *(See page 45.)* While at the bank, make arrangements to change the name on the box, and also on any accounts at that bank. Read important documents in the box and also review documents listed on the *Location of Records* form to make sure that none are missing. If any are missing, telephone or write the appropriate agency and request duplicate records. Not everyone uses a safe deposit box; inspect the document storage box you use, whether it be a safe, tin box, file drawer or shoe box.

NEW WILL

As soon as possible after all changes in assets have been made, prepare, or have prepared, a new will distributing all assets according to your wishes. Be sure to include furniture, collectibles, paintings, cars, boats, sporting and hobby equipment, antiques, and other valuables not covered under most major assets. *(See page 72.)*

DON'T SIGN ANYTHING

Except on very routine matters, don't sign anything, take immediate action or make any quick decisions or commitments on any matter that can wait. You may not be in the right frame of mind for making important, permanent decisions just after the passing of a loved one.

If someone asks you to sign anything that you are not entirely familiar with or sure of, ask to take the document with you so you can study it and think it over. Then, if necessary, seek the advice and opinions of qualified friends and relatives — and, if important enough, discuss with professionals in the field.

Be careful about doing business with people you don't know. Be sure you are dealing with someone who is legitimate and dependable, check references or have someone do this for you before making commitments. With any real estate transactions, large purchases, business decisions, or costly repairs, it is best to do business with known, reputable firms.

DEALING WITH BUREAUCRACIES

To keep the record straight, note the date of phone calls or conversations, the name of the person you spoke with and a brief outline of what was said. If delays in service or any contradictions arise, you will have the facts of your communication available, making it much easier to trace and resolve your problem.

HOUSEHOLD ASSISTANCE

Look in the Yellow Pages under *"Social Services: Information* and *Referral Services"* for support services and agencies listing housekeepers, home health nurses or other service professionals. Hospitals, Health Departments and Hospice organizations are also good referral centers, familiar with available services and eligibility requirements.

GRIEF SUPPORT

AFTER THE MEMORIAL SERVICE and burial is over and everyone goes home to resume their lives again, the survivor might suddenly feel quite alone. It is important to recognize when you need help or company, and to ask for it. Remember to ask family and friends, who want to be there for you, but often feel awkward and don't know what to do.

If you know someone who is grieving the loss of a loved one and are wondering how to help, think of something specific you can do, such as buy groceries, provide child care, or suggest an activity you can participate in together with that person — a movie, ballet, or a walk in the park.

A list of *Support Groups* may be found on page 101. Most funeral homes offer "after-care" services in the form of group or individual grief counseling. Also, *Books for Further Reading* on page 104, suggests reading material which might be comforting during a period of difficult change or bereavement.

Turn to page 100 for some advice on recovering from grief.

PERSONAL LETTER

I THOUGHT THERE SHOULD BE some place for you to leave a personal handwritten letter for your loved one(s). It can be anything you want it to be. The idea came to me after I had filled out all the information in my own version of this book for my wife Kay and our family. I realized that there was one thing missing: a personal message to my family about feelings, emotions and how I hoped everyone would react when that inevitable time came.

Here is a sample letter, just to give you an idea.

Date _____

Dear _____ ,

No one lives forever, so I have decided to complete and leave this legacy to show my love and appreciation for the closeness and love we have shared over the years.

What follows is not included elsewhere in this book, so I hope you will give it serious thought and do your best to carry out my wishes.

As of right now, please try to erase all sad, sorrowful and unhappy thoughts. I am thankful that I have had the joy and happiness of being with you for so many years and I hope you feel that way too.

I am truly grateful for the many blessings I have had during my lifetime: a wonderful wife, children, grandchildren, parents, sisters and brothers and many more blessings others have not been as fortunate to have.

My fondest wish is that you not grieve for very long. Try to think of the good times, the love we've shared and the years we've had together. I would like to see all of you go to someone's house immediately after the church service (not to the cemetery), have something to eat, a couple of drinks and think about and relive some of the happy times we've had together. This might be a good time to show home movies. Make it a joyful family get-together and make plans to have regular family gatherings and continue to enjoy each other's company often.

Please read *Food for Thought* on page 29. It will give you something to think about, and may make it easier for you to get on with your life.

Thank you for making my life all one could ask for.

Love, _____

Write your own letter here or, if you wish, write it somewhere more private and note its location on this page.

A PERSONAL LETTER OF MY THOUGHTS TO:

_____

_____

_____

_____

_____

_____

_____

_____

_____

_____

_____

_____

_____

_____

_____

_____

_____

_____

_____

_____

FAMILY HISTORY

How many generations back does your history extend? If you only know the names of your parents and grandparents, you may find yourself curious enough to do some research and discover more about the roots of your family tree. You might learn some interesting facts which shed light on your own life by checking with older family members.

A legacy of this kind has no financial value, but can be a wealth of riches for you, your children and grandchildren, your great-grandchildren, and so on. It can endow your family with a deeper sense of who they are, how your family has evolved, the changes that time has wrought.

Besides the facts of date and place of births and deaths, you might note:

- Each individual's achievements

- Memories you have of the house or town you grew up in; your grandparents' homes; favorite recipes, holiday traditions, songs, stories

- Important lessons your family has taught you

- Family legends, black sheep

- Family mementoes, the stories behind them

- Any inherited characteristics

- Anything you can think of that might interest future family members

- Location of photographs

Happy the man who thinks of his ancestors with pride, who likes to tell of their deeds and greatness, and rejoices to feel himself linked to the end of their goodly chain.

—Goethe, 1787

There is obviously not enough space here to write your entire family history; but you may begin here then use an additional notebook, and indicate its location here.

FOOD FOR THOUGHT

THERE ARE TWO IMPORTANT DATES in each of our lives. Only one of these is known — our birthday. The second date is our inevitable death, which is unknown.

If an unborn child, safely secure in its mother's womb, were given a choice whether to leave its comfortable surroundings or not, it would probably elect to remain in its present comfortable environment. Yet with no choice, the miracle of birth, the first important date in life, does in fact occur. One is born into an exciting, beautiful world. When the second important date in life arrives, again without choice, is it not possible that a similar miracle could occur?

Caterpillar ... Cocoon ... Butterfly
Can one not believe in miracles?

BENEFITS

"No one wearies of benefits received."
—Marcus Aurelius

IN MANY CASES, survivors are unaware of all the benefits to which they are entitled. Benefits that you are eligible to receive upon retirement are often available to your survivors: Social Security, life insurance and annuities, burial and other benefits for veterans, pension plans or other types of insurance. Completing the forms on the next few pages will make it easier for your survivors to apply.

LIFE INSURANCE

WHILE LIFE INSURANCE cannot eliminate the emotional loss a family feels after a death of a loved one, it helps eliminate the financial hardship that often accompanies such a situation.

Survivors will find great relief in the immediate cash benefits from life insurance policies, and their grief will not be magnified by having to face financial problems at a difficult time.

COMPANY POLICY #	AGENT PHONE #	INSURED BENEFICIARY	PREMIUM DUE DATE	FACE AMOUNT
				$
#				
				$
#				
				$
#				
				$
#				
				$
#				
				$
#				
				$
#				

PENSION, PROFIT-SHARING, KEOGH PLANS, IRAS,

PENSION PLANS, IRAs (Individual Retirement Accounts), and Keogh Plans are all forms of deferred compensation. Knowing how much you will get from these pension plans when you stop working, together with your Social Security income, and income you might receive from other investments, will enable you to plan wisely for your retirement years, and for your survivors.

■ Pension and profit-sharing plans are retirement income benefits partially or completely paid for by your employer during your working years.

■ IRAs are individual retirement bank accounts that can be set up at your bank or savings association.

You can deposit limited funds each year, tax-deferred (at certain income levels), to build a nest egg for retirement over a period of years.

■ Keogh plans are retirement plans for self-employed persons. Keogh Plans have higher contribution limits than IRA accounts.

Consult a tax attorney or your accountant about current allowable contributions, and to decide what is right for you. Tax laws are always changing and everyone's situation is different, requiring different solutions.

TYPE OF PLAN (PENSION, PROFIT-SHARING, IRA, KEOGH)	ADMINISTRATOR/INSTITUTION ADDRESS & PHONE #	MY ID OR ACCOUNT #	% VESTED & VALUE AS OF:
•			___ %
			$
•			___ %
			$
•			___ %
			$
•			___ %
			$
•			___ %
			$

SOCIAL SECURITY

THE MOST IMPORTANT QUESTION about Social Security for young and middle-aged working people is generally the percentage employers will deduct from their paycheck. Those already receiving monthly Social Security payments might be most interested in the possibility of future cost-of-living increases. Survivors will want to know how to file a claim to continue benefits after a death.

Your local Social Security office will answer most of your questions. Check your phone book under *U.S. Government, Health and Human Services Dept.*

NAME	_____
SOCIAL SECURITY #	_____
CARD IS LOCATED	_____
MY BIRTH DATE	_____
PLACE BORN	_____
DATE BENEFITS BEGAN (OR ELIGIBLE TO START)	_____
MONTHLY PAYMENTS (REC'D OR ESTIMATED)	_____
DATES OF MILITARY SERVICE	_____
MY LOCAL SOCIAL SECURITY OFFICE	_____
ADDRESS	_____
	_____
PHONE #	_____

PRIOR SOCIAL SECURITY BENEFITS RECEIVED	❏ YES ❏ NO
IF YES,	❏ BASED ON MY PRIOR EARNINGS
	❏ EARNINGS OF ANOTHER
PRIOR FILE IS LOCATED	_____
OTHER PERSON ENTITLED TO BENEFITS	_____
BIRTH DATE	_____
PLACE BORN	_____
	_____
SOCIAL SECURITY #	_____
DATE BENEFITS BEGAN (OR ELIGIBLE TO START)	_____
MONTHLY PAYMENTS (REC'D OR ESTIMATED)	_____
	_____

MEDICARE FOR PATIENT NOW DECEASED

IF A PERSON COVERED BY MEDICARE has recently passed away, the survivor can bill Medicare for medical expenses incurred before the death, plus a set amount of burial benefits.

Allow sufficient time for final bills to come in from doctors and hospitals. Then send them, together with form HFCA 1660 (sample shown below) to your local Medicare office. Call the 800 number listed under *Health and Human Services Department, Social Security Administration*, in the U.S. Government pages of your phone book to request a copy of the form. It must be signed by

two witnesses and accompany any hospital or medical bills sent in for Medicare payment.

Medicare does not cover the full amount of the bill. If the deceased was covered by a supplemental health policy, you cannot submit a claim to them until the Medicare payment has been received. When you receive it, remove the check and send the bottom portion of the Medicare statement with a claim form and a copy of the bill to your supplemental health insurance carrier. *(See page 38.)*

REQUEST FOR INFORMATION — MEDICARE PAYMENT FOR SERVICES TO A PATIENT NOW DECEASED

No further monies or other benefits may be paid out under this program unless this report is completed and filed as required by existing law and regulations (20 C.F.R. 405 1683).

When completed, send this form to:

Deceased patient

Health insurance claim number of deceased patient

For Services Provided By:

PART I — PAID BILL (If The Bill Is Not Paid Go To Part II)

If bills for medical or other health services were paid by or for the deceased person, Medicare benefits may be due. We hope you will be able to help us determine who should receive payment. The person who paid the deceased's bill(s) has first right to any payment due. If the deceased or his estate paid the bill(s), benefits will be paid to the legal representative of the estate. If there is no legal representative, payment will be made to the person who stands highest in the list of relatives below. If the person who paid the bill(s) dies before being reimbursed, payment is also made to the person standing highest in the list of relatives. If there are no living relatives or legal representatives, no payment will be made. Please answer the questions, sign on the reverse side and return this form in the enclosed envelope.

ALWAYS INCLUDE EVIDENCE OF PAYMENT SUCH AS A RECEIPTED BILL OR OTHER RECEIPT

1. Who paid the deceased's bills for medical or other health services?

☐ The deceased or his estate *(Answer (2) below)*

☐ Yourself *(Sign on reverse side and return form)*

☐ Other person or organization (Enter the person's or organization's name and address in item 4 below. If there is more than one person or organization, attach a listing of names and addresses of these persons or organizations to this form.)

2. Is there a legal representative of the estate?

☐ Yes (If "Yes," print his name and address below. Sign on reverse side and return form.) If you are the legal representative, submit a copy of your appointment papers with this form.

☐ No (If "No," answer item 3 below.)

3. This item is answered only if item 2 above is checked "No". Put a check in the box next to the living relative that stands highest on the following list and then write that relative's name and address in item 4 below. (If you check the box for child or children and there is more than one child, attach a listing of the names and address of all the children to this form.)

☐ Widow or widower living in the same household as the deceased at the time of death, or entitled to a monthly Social Security or Railroad Retirement benefit on the same earnings record as the deceased in the month of death.

☐ A child or children of the deceased entitled to monthly Social Security or Railroad Retirement benefits or the same earnings record as the deceased in the month of death. *(List the names and addresses of all entitled children of the deceased)*

☐ A parent or parents of the deceased entitled to monthly Social Security or Railroad Retirement benefits on the same earnings record as the deceased in the month of death.

☐ A widow or widower who was neither living with the deceased at the time of death nor at that time entitled on the same earnings record to a Social Security or Railroad Retirement benefit.

☐ A child or children of the deceased who were not entitled in the month of death to monthly Social Security or Railroad Retirement benefits on the same earnings record as the deceased. *(List the names and addresses of all such children)*

☐ A parent or parents not entitled in the month of death to monthly Social Security or Railroad Retirement benefits on the same earnings record as the deceased.

4. Name   Address

FORM HCFA-1660 (8-81)   DESTROY PRIOR EDITIONS   Continued On Back

---

PART II — UNPAID BILL (If The Bill Is Paid, Complete Part I)

When the beneficiary has died and a physician or supplier does not agree to accept the reasonable charge as the full charge, payment may be made on the basis of an unpaid bill to the person who has agreed to assume legal liability to pay the physician or supplier.

If you are assuming such legal liability and want to claim Medicare benefits for the services furnished to the deceased beneficiary, you must furnish the documents listed below to us and sign this form below. Your signature below certifies to the following statement:

I have assumed the legal obligation to pay the physician or supplier named below for services furnished to the deceased beneficiary on the date(s) indicated. I hereby claim any Medicare benefits due for these services.

Name of Physician or Supplier	Name of Deceased Beneficiary	Date(s) of Services

In addition furnish the following documents together with this form to us.

1. A completed form HCFA-1490S, PATIENT'S REQUEST FOR MEDICARE PAYMENTS. You must sign item 6 of the HCFA-1490S in lieu of the deceased beneficiary. (You may obtain a copy of the HCFA-1490S from a Social Security Office if you did not receive one with this form;) and

2. A signed statement from the physician or supplier which shows that the physician or supplier refuses to accept assignment for the bill; and

3. An itemized bill from the physician or supplier which identifies you as the person to whom the physician or supplier looks for payment.

Sign below and return this form together with the documents specified above to the address shown in the upper left portion of the form on the other side. If no carrier name and address is shown on the other side of this form request the proper addressee information from a Social Security Office.

I certify that if I receive the entire amount due, I will distribute it among other persons if they are legally entitled to it. Knowing that anyone making a false statement or representation of a material fact for use in determining the right to or the amount of Health Insurance benefits commits a crime punishable under the Federal law. I certify that the above statements are true.

If this statement has been signed by mark (X), two witnesses who know the claimant should sign below, giving their full addresses. The signature and title of a Social Security employee will suffice in lieu of signatures of two witnesses.	Name of claimant *(Please print)*
Name	Signature of claimant *(Write in ink)* **SIGN HERE** ▶
Address *(Number and Street, City, State and ZIP Code)*	Mailing Address *(Number and Street, P.O. Box or Route)*
Name	City, State and ZIP Code
Address *(Number and Street, City, State and ZIP Code)*	Date *(Month, Day and Year)* Telephone number

If you wish assistance in completing this request, please take it to a Social Security Office. The people there will help you.
PLEASE RETURN THIS REQUEST IN THE ENCLOSED ENVELOPE

HCFA-1660 (8-81)   ☆ U.S.GPO 1988- 201-812/81315

Note: This form has been reduced here. It is a sample only and is not meant to be filled out.

MEDICARE AND SUPPLEMENTAL MEDICAL CLAIMS

Including health, accident, travel and disability claims

IN ADDITION TO RECEIVING monthly paychecks, the taxes you have paid into the Social Security system all these years also finance Survivor Benefits, Disability Benefits, and Medicare. The Medicare program consists of Part A, Hospital Insurance, and for a low monthly premium you can also subscribe to Part B, Medical Insurance Outside the Hospital, which covers a portion of doctor bills, medical supplies, home health care and other outpatient treatment.

■ Part A covers 40-50% of your medical bills.

■ Part B will reimburse you for another 20-25%.

I strongly recommend applying to a private insurance carrier for supplemental (to Medicare) insurance coverage. Or, if possible, continue a policy upon your retirement, if you have been previously covered under a group program through your employer.

Information Normally Required to Complete Medical Claims

MEDICARE

SUPPLEMENTAL INSURANCE
(see page 38)

ADDRESS _____

NAME OF CARRIER _____

_____

ADDRESS _____

PHONE # _____

_____

PATIENT'S SS # _____

PHONE # _____

PATIENT'S BIRTH DATE _____

PATIENT'S ID # _____

DATE MEDICARE INITIALLY STARTED _____

CODE # _____

GROUP PLAN # _____

Make photocopies of all claims paid by Medicare if they are to be sent to supplemental insurance carriers. Keep copies as they will be required if you are questioned later. At the end of the year, add up your health insurance premiums, all of your

deductibles, dental and eye doctors' costs, drugs and any other medical costs not paid for by your insurance plans. Check latest tax laws to determine if total qualifies for income tax deduction.

MEDICAL CLAIMS RECORD

			MEDICARE		SUPPLEMENTAL			
DATE OF SERVICE	DOCTOR OR OTHER	DESCRIPTION OF SERVICE	AMOUNT OF CLAIM	AMOUNT PAID	DATE TO SUPP. INS.	AMOUNT OF CLAIM	AMOUNT PAID	TOTAL NOT PAID

TOTAL OF COLUMN
NOT PAID BY MEDICARE OR
SUPPLEMENTAL INSURANCE
(includes deductible amounts) _____

TOTAL OTHER MEDICAL EXPENSES
FOR YEAR, NOT SHOWN ABOVE
(glasses, dental, prescriptions, etc.) _____

TOTAL YEARLY PREMIUMS _____

TOTAL FOR YEAR _____
(may qualify for tax deduction)

SUPPLEMENTAL MEDICAL INSURANCE

Other than Medicare

WE ALL KNOW that medical costs today are astronomical. While insurance may be costly, serious illness involving hospitalization can be financially devastating. Medicare provides coverage on a limited basis at age 65 *(see page 36),* and can be supplemented by individual plans.

- **BASIC COVERAGE** will pay some part of hospital bills, surgery and doctors' fees not covered by Medicare.

- **MAJOR MEDICAL** picks up where basic coverage leaves off.

- **COINSURANCE** means you bear part of the cost of medical bills.

- **HMO PLANS** allow for medical services whenever you need them for a monthly or quarterly fee paid in advance, using doctors from a list of participating HMO-employed physicians.

COMPANY NAME _____

COMPANY POLICY # _____

AGENT NAME _____

AGENT PHONE # _____

NAME OF INSURED _____

DESCRIPTION OF BENEFITS _____

TYPE OF INSURANCE _____

POLICY LIMIT _____

AMOUNT OF PREMIUM _____

PREMIUM DUE DATE _____

COMPANY NAME _____

COMPANY POLICY # _____

AGENT NAME _____

AGENT PHONE # _____

NAME OF INSURED _____

DESCRIPTION OF BENEFITS _____

TYPE OF INSURANCE _____

POLICY LIMIT _____

AMOUNT OF PREMIUM _____

PREMIUM DUE DATE _____

LOCATION OF POLICIES _____

DATE FIRST COMPLETED _____

DATE REVISED _____

MEDICAL HISTORY

USE THIS FORM to document medical conditions you or family members have that might be inherited and passed on, such as heart disease, gout, cancer, high blood pressure, arthritis, etc. It's also a good idea to note whether anyone has had measles, German measles, chicken pox, or other childhood sicknesses that may have serious consequences for adults. You may also keep a record here of accidents, for insurance and other purposes.

NAME OF PERSON	NAME OF ILLNESS	DATE

VETERANS' BENEFITS

Veterans' benefits for those who qualify include:

- Life insurance
- Medical care
- Disability compensation
- Pensions
- Home mortgages
- Rehabilitation centers
- Job training
- Educational assistance
- Burial and other death benefits

If you or a family member (alive or deceased) qualify as a veteran, toll-free telephone service is available in all fifty states. Check your phone book under *U.S. Government, Veterans Administration.*

For more information or to receive a free booklet called *A Summary of Veterans Administration Benefits*, write or phone your local *One Stop Veterans Assistance Center* regional office.

NARRATIVE HISTORY OF MILITARY SERVICE _____

_____

_____

DATE OF BIRTH _____	DATE ENTERED ACTIVE SERVICE _____
PLACE OF BIRTH _____	PLACE _____
SOCIAL SECURITY # _____	SERVICE NUMBER _____
V.A. FILE # _____	DATE SEPARATED _____
LOCAL V.A. OFFICE _____	PLACE _____
ADDRESS _____	GRADE OR RANK AND BRANCH _____
_____	MILITARY DECORATIONS _____
PHONE # _____	
ELIGIBLE TO RECEIVE PENSION ON (DATE) _____	LOCATION OF SEPARATION PAPERS _____
IF SPOUSE ELIGIBLE, AMOUNT OF PENSION _____	_____

WORKERS' COMPENSATION

YOUR EMPLOYER'S Workers' Compensation Insurance will provide medical and death benefits in some cases. This varies from state to state and from policy to policy. If a work-related injury, illness or death has occurred, be sure to consult the employer of that person for possible recompense. If you've never had a work-related claim or injury, you don't need to complete this form.

NAME OF INSURED _____

NATURE OF INJURY _____

DATE INJURED _____

INSURANCE CARRIER _____

ADDRESS _____

_____

PHONE # _____

CLAIM # _____

PAYMENTS MADE _____

DATE & DURATION _____

EMPLOYER AT TIME OF INJURY _____

ADDRESS _____

_____

PHONE # _____

NAME OF INSURED _____

NATURE OF INJURY _____

DATE INJURED _____

INSURANCE CARRIER _____

ADDRESS _____

_____

PHONE # _____

CLAIM # _____

PAYMENTS MADE _____

DATE & DURATION _____

EMPLOYER AT TIME OF INJURY _____

ADDRESS _____

_____

PHONE # _____

ASSETS AND LIABILITIES

CHANCES ARE you have made various investments over the course of your life. You probably have a savings account, you may have invested in mutual funds or have a second mortgage. You have more than likely made these investment choices based on years of experience, talking to professional advisors and by studying the market. The forms on the following pages provide a single place to document information on all your investments.

As you fill in the information, locate the applicable documents and store them in a single place, rather than leaving them scattered throughout the house in drawers or safe deposit boxes (or shoe boxes). Record the location of these documents in the *Location of Records* form on page 14. Use the *Notes* area on the forms to include your recommendations on how survivors should proceed with these investments, and whom to contact for advice when needed.

And tell those who should know.

BANKS, SAVINGS & LOAN ACCOUNTS

Including T-bills, CDs

NAME OF BANK _____   TYPE OF ACCOUNT _____

ADDRESS _____   ACCOUNT # _____

_____   IN WHOSE NAME(S) _____

CONTACT PERSON _____   BALANCE _____

PHONE # _____   AS OF DATE _____

NAME OF BANK _____   TYPE OF ACCOUNT _____

ADDRESS _____   ACCOUNT # _____

_____   IN WHOSE NAME(S) _____

CONTACT PERSON _____   BALANCE _____

PHONE # _____   AS OF DATE _____

NAME OF BANK _____   TYPE OF ACCOUNT _____

ADDRESS _____   ACCOUNT # _____

_____   IN WHOSE NAME(S) _____

CONTACT PERSON _____   BALANCE _____

PHONE # _____   AS OF DATE _____

SAFE DEPOSIT BOX INFORMATION

Safe deposit keys cannot be duplicated; it is important to keep these keys in a safe place.

BOX #1

NAME OF BANK _____   KEY IS LOCATED _____

BRANCH _____   CONTENTS _____

SIGNATURES _____   _____

_____   _____

BOX #2

NAME OF BANK _____   KEY IS LOCATED _____

BRANCH _____   CONTENTS _____

SIGNATURES _____   _____

_____   _____

BOX #3

NAME OF BANK _____   KEY IS LOCATED _____

BRANCH _____   CONTENTS _____

SIGNATURES _____   _____

_____   _____

Comedian W.C. Fields was an extreme case. Memories of his impoverished youth brought Fields recurring nightmares about being stranded in a strange city without funds. The wealthy performer recalled opening as many as 700 bank accounts, often in fictitious names, in the cities he visited around the world. Fields left no record for his heirs and only 48 of his bank accounts were located after his death. Over a million dollars of his estate is thought to have remained scattered in hundreds of undiscovered bank accounts.

–David S. Magee
Everything Your Heirs Need to Know About You

INVESTMENTS: STOCKS, BONDS, INVESTMENT FUNDS

Including money market, mutual funds, government securities, limited partnerships, annuities

NAME & ADDRESS OF INVESTMENT FIRM	CONTACT PERSON & PHONE #	ACCOUNT #	SECURITY DESCRIPTION (NAME OF STOCK, FUND, ETC.)

In Whose Name(s)	# of Shares	Date Bought	Cost Per Share	Total Cost	Divid. Per Share	Date Paid	Total Dividend	Value As of

REAL ESTATE: HOME, INVESTMENT PROPERTIES, OTHER ASSETS

See page 50 for mortgage and loan details.

DESCRIPTION OF PROPERTY	ADDRESS OF PROPERTY	PROPERTY MGR	CONTACT PHONE #

% OF OWNER- SHIP	DEED IN NAME OF	DATE ACQUIRED	COST BASIS	COST OF IMPROVE- MENTS	PRESENT MARKET VALUE	AS OF DATE	MONTHLY INCOME	DUE DATE

NOTES, FIRST OR SECOND MORTGAGES, OTHER LIABILITIES: WE OWE

Including home mortgage, investment properties, business, auto, and personal loans

DESCRIPTION OF LOAN	NAME OF LENDER	ADDRESS	PHONE #

AMOUNT OF LOAN	DATE LOAN MADE	DATE TOTAL DUE	% INT.	BAL. OF DEBT	AS OF DATE	PMT. AMT.	DATE PMT. DUE	PROPERTY TAXES	DATE TAXES DUE

NOTES, FIRST OR SECOND MORTGAGES, OTHER ASSETS: OWED TO US

Including interest in a business, investment properties, mortgages or other loans made

DESCRIPTION OF LOAN	NAME OF DEBTOR	ADDRESS	PHONE #

AMOUNT OF LOAN	SECURITY OR COLLATERAL	DATE LOAN MADE	% INT.	PMT. AMT.	DATE PMT. DUE	FINAL PMT. DUE

INVESTMENT POSSIBILITIES FOR SURVIVORS

INSURANCE PROCEEDS and other benefits due to a survivor at the time of a death can be considerable. What do you have in mind for your spouse, children or other beneficiaries? What will they do with that check for $10,000, $20,000, $50,000, $100,000? Should it be in the bank at 5%, or be distributed periodically to your heirs in monthly or quarterly installments? Maybe you have an idea about safe stocks or bonds that have a good yield and a chance for growth. It is a good idea to discuss the possibilities with your spouse or beneficiary. Some options are:

- Tax-free money market and mutual funds

- Taxable money market and mutual funds

- Treasury bills (T-bills)

- Certificates of deposit (CDs) with fixed yield for safety

- Long-term tax-free municipal bonds

- Intermediate-term tax-free municipal bonds

- Government money market mutual funds

- Treasury or high-grade corporate bond funds

- Ginnie Mae mutual funds

- IRA

- Common or preferred stock

- Real estate

- Limited partnership

- Gold shares

- Others

Write down some of your suggestions here:

Notes

FINANCIAL PLANNING

"Thinking about money is an activity which can send one into a state that borders on anything from slight uneasiness to terror."

—Irwin Shaw, *Bread Upon the Waters*

FINANCIAL PLANNING is not only for those with considerable assets. Whether you have few or large holdings or assets, you want to manage them wisely now and in the future, and leave a sensible and orderly plan for your eventual survivors.

Because it is a difficult and complicated subject, it is not the intent of this book to have you develop a complete financial plan here. On the other hand, by reviewing and completing the forms on the following pages, you can accomplish a great deal that will be rewarding for both your survivors and yourself. At a glance, you will be able to determine the amounts and sources of your present monthly income and expenses. Planning your future income and expenses will provide a basis of operation for your survivors when they will have to handle all financial responsibilities without you.

Depending on the size and complexity of your particular situation, the use of professional planners may be in order. If so, they will generally be well worth the expense.

PRESENT/FUTURE MONTHLY INCOME

SOURCE OF INCOME	PRESENT INCOME AS OF DATE:	ANTICIPATED INCOME AT RETIREMENT	ANTICIPATED INCOME FOR SURVIVORS	SEE PAGE
SALARY (INCLUDE BONUS)				
SELF-EMPLOYED EARNINGS				
PROFESSIONAL FEES				
SOCIAL SECURITY				34
PENSION				33
IRA				33
KEOGH				33
PROFIT-SHARING				33
LOAN/NOTE PAYMENTS —TO US				52
TRUST FUNDS				
LIFE INSURANCE ANNUITIES				32
LIFE INSURANCE PROCEEDS				32
OTHER ANNUITIES				46
DIVIDENDS				46
INTEREST INCOME				52
SUBTOTAL *(carry over to next page)*	$	$	$	

Source of Income	Present Income as of Date: _____	Anticipated Income at Retirement	Anticipated Income for Survivors	See Page
Mutual/Money Funds				44, 46
Veterans' Benefits				40
Union Benefits				
Rental Income				48
Partnership Income				46
Royalties				52
Other Income				
Subtotal (this page)	$	$	$	
Subtotal (from page 58)	$	$	$	
Total Monthly Income	$	$	$	
Total Annual Income (multiply x 12)	$	$	$	

Enter total on "Present/Future Annual Income/Expenses Summary" on page 62.

NOTES

_____

_____

_____

DATE COMPLETED

_____

PRESENT/FUTURE MONTHLY EXPENSES

Does not include federal, state and Social Security taxes *(see page 62)*.

TYPE OF EXPENSE	PRESENT EXPENSE AS OF DATE:	ANTICIPATED EXPENSE AT RETIREMENT	ANTICIPATED EXPENSE FOR SURVIVORS	SEE PAGE
MORTGAGE (INCLUDE INTEREST)				50
RENT				
PERSONAL LOANS/NOTES				50
AUTO LOAN(S)				50
OTHER LOAN(S)				50
PROPERTY TAXES				50
HOMEOWNERS OR RENTERS INSURANCE				70
LIFE INSURANCE				32
MEDICAL INSURANCE				38
AUTO INSURANCE				70
FOOD, SUNDRIES, HOUSEHOLD GOODS				
CLOTHING				
PHONE				
GAS/ELECTRIC				
WATER				
GARBAGE				
SUBTOTAL *(carry over to next page)*	$	$	$	

TYPE OF EXPENSE	PRESENT EXPENSE AS OF DATE:	ANTICIPATED EXPENSE AT RETIREMENT	ANTICIPATED EXPENSE FOR SURVIVORS	SEE PAGE
AUTO GAS, OIL, REPAIRS, REGISTRATION				
BUS FARE, PARKING, TOLLS				
HOME REPAIRS & MAINTENANCE				48
COLLEGE/EDUCATION				
CHILD CARE/ SUPPORT TO DEPENDENTS				
CHARITABLE CONTRIBUTIONS				
ENTERTAINMENT, CLUB DUES, MEALS OUT				
CREDIT CARDS (TOTAL ALL CARDS)				15
MEDICAL EXPENSES				37
TV, NEWSPAPERS, MAGAZINES				
TRAVEL, VACATION				
OTHER NON-RECURRING EXPENSES				
SUBTOTAL (this page)	$	$	$	
SUBTOTAL (from page 60)	$	$	$	
TOTAL MONTHLY EXPENSES	$	$	$	
TOTAL ANNUAL EXPENSES (multiply x 12)	$	$	$	

Enter total on "Present/Future Annual Income/Expenses Summary" on page 62.

PRESENT/FUTURE ANNUAL INCOME/EXPENSES SUMMARY

	PRESENT AS OF	ANTICIPATED AT RETIREMENT	ANTICIPATED FOR SURVIVORS
TOTAL ANNUAL INCOME *(from page 59)*	$	$	$
LESS FEDERAL, STATE & SOCIAL SECURITY TAXES	$	$	$
SPENDABLE ANNUAL INCOME	$	$	$
LESS ANNUAL EXPENSES *(from page 61)*	$	$	$
DIFFERENCE *(Review plus or minus figure and take appropriate action)*	$	$	$

NAME OF ACCOUNTANT OR CPA _____

ADDRESS _____

_____

PHONE # _____

NAME OF FINANCIAL PLANNER _____

ADDRESS _____

_____

PHONE # _____

NOTES

_____

_____

_____

_____

_____

NOTES

PRESENT/FUTURE ASSETS

ASSET	PRESENT VALUE AS OF	ANTICIPATED VALUE AT RETIREMENT	ANTICIPATED VALUE FOR SURVIVORS	SEE PAGE
CASH ON HAND (BANKS, S&L, OTHER ACCTS.)				44
STOCKS, BONDS, INVESTMENT FUNDS				46
CDS, T-BILLS				44
MARKET VALUE OF HOME				48
INVESTMENT PROPERTIES				48
NOTES, MORTGAGES (OWED TO US)				52
PENSION, PROFIT-SHARING, IRA, KEOGH				33
OTHER INVESTMENTS (LIMITED PARTNERSHIP, ETC.)				46
OTHER LIQUID ASSETS				44
AUTOMOBILE(S), OTHER VEHICLES				77
LIFE INSURANCE CASH VALUE				32
LIFE INSURANCE DEATH BENEFIT				32
ANNUITIES				32, 46
INTEREST IN A BUSINESS				52
SUBTOTALS (carry over to next page)	$	$	$	

Asset	Present Value As of	Anticipated Value At Retirement	Anticipated Value for Survivors	See Page
Household Furnishings & Appliances				72–75
Furs & Jewelry				77
Precious Metals				77
Collectibles				77
Sports & Hobby Equipment				76
Art, Antiques				72
Tools				76
Other Assets				
Subtotal *(this page)*	$	$	$	
Subtotal *(from page 64)*	$	$	$	
Total Value of Assets *(carry over to page 68, Net Worth Summary)*	$	$	$	

PRESENT/FUTURE LIABILITIES

LIABILITY	OWED AS OF DATE	OWED AT RETIREMENT	OWED BY SURVIVORS	SEE PAGE
BUSINESS LOAN(S)				50
HOME MORTGAGE(S)				50
OTHER REAL ESTATE LOAN(S)				50
AUTO LOAN(S)				50
PERSONAL LOAN(S)				50
PROPERTY TAXES				50
ANNUAL INCOME TAX				62
SUBTOTAL *(carry over to next page)*	$	$	$	

LIABILITY	OWED AS OF DATE	OWED AT RETIREMENT	OWED BY SURVIVORS	SEE PAGE
ESTATE TAXES				
LIFE INSURANCE LOAN(S)				
INSTALLMENT LOAN(S)				50
BANK CREDIT CARDS				15, 61
MEDICAL BILLS				37
DEPARTMENT STORE BILLS				61
OUTSTANDING BILLS				
OTHER LIABILITIES				
SUBTOTAL *(this page)*	$	$	$	
SUBTOTAL *(from page 66)*	$	$	$	
TOTAL LIABILITIES *(carry over to page 68, Net Worth Summary)*	$	$	$	

PRESENT/FUTURE NET WORTH SUMMARY

THIS PAGE IS DESIGNED for easy access, to make changes and update periodically (for example, at annual income tax preparation time.) Complete only the columns that apply to your current circumstances. Your annual net worth records will provide an ongoing picture of how you are managing your financial, personal and other resources.

Complete form in pencil!

Show the letter "E" for "Estimated Value", "A" for "Actual Value."

	PRESENT TOTALS YEAR: ___	ANTICIPATED TOTALS AT RETIREMENT	ANTICIPATED TOTALS FOR SURVIVORS
TOTAL ASSETS (from page 65)	$	$	$
TOTAL LIABILITIES (from page 67)	$	$	$
NET WORTH (subtract liabilities from assets)	$	$	$

	PRESENT TOTALS YEAR: ___	ANTICIPATED TOTALS AT RETIREMENT	ANTICIPATED TOTALS FOR SURVIVORS
TOTAL ASSETS (from page 65)	$	$	$
TOTAL LIABILITIES (from page 67)	$	$	$
NET WORTH (subtract liabilities from assets)	$	$	$

	PRESENT TOTALS YEAR: ___	ANTICIPATED TOTALS AT RETIREMENT	ANTICIPATED TOTALS FOR SURVIVORS
TOTAL ASSETS (from page 65)	$	$	$
TOTAL LIABILITIES (from page 67)	$	$	$
NET WORTH (subtract liabilities from assets)	$	$	$

	PRESENT TOTALS YEAR:	ANTICIPATED TOTALS AT RETIREMENT	ANTICIPATED TOTALS FOR SURVIVORS
TOTAL ASSETS *(from page 65)*	$	$	$
TOTAL LIABILITIES *(from page 67)*	$	$	$
NET WORTH *(subtract liabilities from assets)*	$	$	$

	PRESENT TOTALS YEAR:	ANTICIPATED TOTALS AT RETIREMENT	ANTICIPATED TOTALS FOR SURVIVORS
TOTAL ASSETS *(from page 65)*	$	$	$
TOTAL LIABILITIES *(from page 67)*	$	$	$
NET WORTH *(subtract liabilities from assets)*	$	$	$

	PRESENT TOTALS YEAR:	ANTICIPATED TOTALS AT RETIREMENT	ANTICIPATED TOTALS FOR SURVIVORS
TOTAL ASSETS *(from page 65)*	$	$	$
TOTAL LIABILITIES *(from page 67)*	$	$	$
NET WORTH *(subtract liabilities from assets)*	$	$	$

INSURANCE: HOMEOWNERS, RENTERS, AUTO

WE BUY INSURANCE to protect us from the consequences of damage to property, loss of life, injuries, illness and disability — all things we don't like to think about. Many of us put our insurance problems at the bottom of our priority list, because there are "more important things to do," more tangible things. But buy some "bad" insurance — or none at all — and in the event of an uninsured loss, your life savings could go down the drain.

If you own your own home, you probably have a Homeowners policy. This not only covers your home (the structure) and your personal property (its contents) against destruction by fire, theft, vandalism, and other causes, it also protects you against lawsuits arising from accidents: a slip-and-fall mishap on your premises, a dog biting a guest, a sports injury. If you are renting a house, apartment, or condominium, you can purchase a Renters policy to cover your personal property and liability exposure.

Your largest personal insurance exposure is probably your automobile. There are few drivers who have not at one time or another been in an automobile accident. Many such accidents are merely "fender benders" and only involve damage to the cars. Once in a while though, serious accidents occur and result in injuries and even death. If you are negligent in such an instance, you can be sued for a great deal, even millions of dollars, for injuries and damages.

Record addresses of property insured and license numbers of cars on this form, and note the location of applicable documents on the *Location of Records* form on page 14.

NOTES

INSURANCE

AGENT NAME COMPANY NAME	ADDRESS & PHONE #	TYPE OF POLICY	POLICY #	TERM EXP. DATE	ANNUAL PREMIUM	PREM. DUE DATE
•						
•						
•						
•						
•						
•						

HOME AND PERSONAL PROPERTY INVENTORY

BEGIN WITH THE ROOM you're sitting in. Look around. What would happen to all these things if you suddenly were gone? Are your children or heirs going to know how valuable that furniture is? Or your family heirlooms? Who should get it? Or should it be sold? If it's sold, how much is it worth?

Although only a will is legally binding, a list is a practical way of handling the distribution of personal property, and may avoid the necessity of a separate listing and appraisal of every item in a probate proceeding. Making this household inventory now will give you the opportunity to state the value of each item in your household and suggest who should inherit it.

Conducting a home inventory is also essential in determining if the amount of insurance you have on your personal property is adequate. And besides these practical purposes, you might even be pleasantly surprised to discover the total value of your possessions.

While you're at it, go through your belongings. Over the years we all become collectors and keep things we feel we (or others) will have use for in the future. Try this: at your leisure, clean out your closets, desks, files, drawers, attic, basement, garage, medicine cabinet, kitchen cabinets, all the little storage areas of your home. Do this a little at a time. Consider (as much as it hurts) getting rid of things you know you will never need or use. Give usable items to children, charitable organizations, friends, or have a garage sale. Itemize all items you give to charity and get a signed receipt for a possible tax deduction.

And remember, when in doubt, throw it out!

LIVING ROOM

ITEM	VALUE	HEIR
RUGS	$	
COUCH/CHAIRS	$	
CHESTS	$	
DESK	$	
BOOKCASES BOOKS	$	
DRAPES & CURTAINS	$	
LAMPS	$	
COFFEE/END TABLES	$	
CLOCKS/ MIRRORS	$	
PAINTINGS/ ART OBJECTS	$	
STEREO/RADIO	$	
TV/VCR	$	
PIANO/ORGAN	$	
FIREPLACE FIXTURES	$	
ANTIQUES	$	
OTHER	$	
TOTAL	$	DATE:

KITCHEN

ITEM	VALUE	HEIR
REFRIGERATOR	$	
FREEZER	$	
STOVE	$	
MICROWAVE	$	
DISHWASHER	$	
POTS & PANS	$	
DISHES	$	
COOKING IMPLEMENTS	$	
SMALL APPLIANCES	$	
SILVERWARE	$	
OTHER	$	
	$	
	$	
	$	
	$	
TOTAL	$	DATE:

DINING ROOM

ITEM	VALUE	HEIR
RUGS	$	
DINING ROOM SET	$	
CHINA CABINET	$	
SERVING TABLES	$	
ELECTRIC UTENSILS	$	
TABLE LINEN	$	
SILVERWARE	$	
CHINA	$	
DISHES	$	
GLASSWARE	$	
DECORATIONS	$	
OTHER	$	
	$	
	$	
	$	
TOTAL	$	DATE:

BEDROOM #1   BEDROOM #2   BEDROOM #3

ITEM	VALUE	HEIR	VALUE	HEIR	VALUE	HEIR
BEDS	$		$		$	
MATTRESSES & SPRINGS	$		$		$	
CHESTS	$		$		$	
DRESSING TABLES	$		$		$	
DESK & CONTENTS	$		$		$	
DRAPES CURTAINS	$		$		$	
RUGS	$		$		$	
LAMPS & RADIOS	$		$		$	
CHAIRS	$		$		$	
BLANKETS & SPREADS	$		$		$	
LINEN	$		$		$	
PAINTINGS	$		$		$	
WALL HANGINGS	$		$		$	
MIRRORS	$		$		$	
OTHER	$		$		$	
	$		$		$	
TOTAL	$	DATE:	$	DATE:	$	DATE:

GUEST ROOM

ITEM	VALUE	HEIR
BEDS	$	
MATTRESSES & SPRINGS	$	
CHESTS	$	
DRESSING TABLES	$	
DESK & CONTENTS	$	
DRAPES & CURTAINS	$	
RUGS	$	
LAMPS & RADIOS	$	
CHAIRS	$	
MIRRORS	$	
BLANKETS & SPREADS	$	
LINEN	$	
PICTURES	$	
OTHER	$	
	$	
	$	
TOTAL	$	DATE:

FAMILY ROOM

ITEM	VALUE	HEIR
RUGS	$	
TV/VCR	$	
STEREO	$	
RECORDS/ TAPES/CDS	$	
RADIO	$	
COUCH	$	
CHAIRS	$	
TABLES	$	
PAINTINGS	$	
WALL HANGINGS	$	
COMPUTER	$	
OTHER	$	
	$	
	$	
	$	
TOTAL	$	DATE:

SPORTS AND HOBBY

ITEM	VALUE	HEIR
BICYCLES	$	
GOLF CLUBS	$	
MUSICAL INSTRUMENTS	$	
FISHING RODS	$	
BOATS & MOTORS	$	
CAMERAS & LENSES	$	
TENNIS EQUIPMENT	$	
GUNS	$	
HOBBY EQUIPMENT	$	
CAMPING EQUIPMENT	$	
OTHER	$	
	$	
	$	
	$	
	$	
	$	
TOTAL	$	DATE:

GARAGE-BASEMENT-ATTIC

ITEM	VALUE	HEIR
FURNITURE STORED	$	
WASHING MACHINE	$	
DRYER	$	
POWER TOOLS	$	
OTHER TOOLS	$	
CANNED GOODS	$	
TRUNKS & LUGGAGE	$	
WORK BENCH	$	
SUPPLIES	$	
GARDEN TOOLS	$	
LAWN MOWER	$	
SHELVING	$	
OTHER	$	
	$	
	$	
TOTAL	$	DATE:

HOME OFFICE/MISCELLANEOUS

ITEM	VALUE	HEIR
FURNITURE	$	
FILE CABINETS	$	
COMPUTER EQUIPMENT	$	
OFFICE MACHINES	$	
CARS	$	
	$	
MOTORCYCLES	$	
BOAT	$	
COLLECTIBLES	$	
FURS & JEWELRY	$	
PRECIOUS METALS	$	
OTHER	$	
	$	
	$	
	$	
	$	
TOTAL	$	DATE:

RECAP OF TOTAL VALUE OF HOME INVENTORY

ITEM	VALUE	HEIR
LIVING ROOM	$	
KITCHEN	$	
DINING ROOM	$	
BEDROOM #1	$	
BEDROOM #2	$	
BEDROOM #3	$	
GUEST ROOM	$	
FAMILY ROOM	$	
SPORTS & HOBBY	$	
GARAGE ATTIC	$	
HOME OFFICE/ MISC.	$	
	$	
	$	
	$	
	$	
GRAND TOTAL	$	DATE:

CONTACTS FOR
SALE OF ASSETS

LATER, THE SURVIVOR MAY WISH to consider the sale of certain assets. The benefactor may want to recommend which items to sell, at what estimated price, and to whom. Coordinate this list with your *Home and Personal Property Inventory (see pages 72–77)* and other investment and planning forms in this book.

ITEM	ESTIMATED VALUE	AS OF DATE	HEIR OR CONTACT FOR SALE	PHONE #
HOME	$			
	$			
INVESTMENT PROPERTIES	$			
	$			
BUSINESS: SOLE PROPRIETORSHIP	$			
	$			
LIMITED PARTNERSHIP	$			
CORPORATION	$			
BUSINESS PROPERTY	$			
	$			
STOCKS, BONDS	$			
	$			
OTHER INVESTMENTS	$			
	$			

ITEM	ESTIMATED VALUE	AS OF DATE	HEIR OR CONTACT FOR SALE	PHONE #
VEHICLES	$			
	$			
FURNITURE	$			
	$			
TOOLS	$			
SPORTS & HOBBY EQUIPMENT	$			
	$			
COLLECTIBLES	$			
	$			
ANTIQUES	$			
PAINTINGS/ ART OBJECTS	$			
MUSICAL INSTRUMENTS	$			
FURS & JEWELRY	$			
CLUB MEMBERSHIPS	$			
OTHER	$			
	$			
	$			

FINANCIAL TIPS

Tax laws often change. Check with your advisor before committing yourself to a move which may have tax consequences.

■ **PRINCIPAL RESIDENCE** If you are 55 or over and have sold or want to sell your principal residence (in which you have lived for three or more years), you may exclude up to $125,000 in profit from your income tax. Either spouse must be age 55 or older to qualify. This tax break is a once-in-a-lifetime benefit for the taxpayer. A tax advantage like this could provide capital for other investments, or for renting or purchasing a smaller home, or other needs.

Whenever you sell your principal residence and buy another of equal or greater value within 24 months, you do not need to report the gain on the sale until the sale of the newly acquired residence. There are no age requirements involved.

■ **DEFER PROPERTY TAXES** Those over 65 may be able to defer annual property taxes. All accrued taxes may be paid whenever the property is sold. Contact local officials for more details regarding this matter.

■ **TAP HOME EQUITY** Persons with considerable equity in their home can, under certain conditions, tap this equity and receive monthly payments. This alternative is not for everyone. Contact your bank for further information.

■ **REFINANCING EXISTING MORTGAGES** A rule of thumb for refinancing any existing mortgage is to watch the home mortgage interest rates and consider refinancing when the going rate is 2% below what you are currently paying. There are costs involved in refinancing, so you will want to be sure that the proposed interest savings will exceed those costs when spread over the time period you are likely to own that home.

■ **REVERSE MORTGAGES** Many seniors are using reverse mortgages as a way to tap home equity without having to move. They work just like a regular mortgage but instead of getting a lump sum that you must immediately start paying off, you usually get monthly payments that needn't be repaid until the end of the loan term. Principal and interest charges simply accumulate until the loan is due, often at the time of the borrower's death. Drawbacks range from high fees and expenses to the inaccessibility of these types of loans in many parts of the country. Reverse mortgage guides and lender lists are available for free from the *American Association of Retired Persons* (AARP), 601 E Street NW, Washington, DC 20049. For cash-poor, home equity-rich seniors, reverse mortgages can be a key to a more comfortable retirement.

■ **NAME CHANGES AND TRANSFER OF TITLES** If you wish to keep your estate (at least some parts of your estate) out of probate court, it is important to make sure that title to your home and other property can be transferred without probate. In some states, this can be done by holding property as "community property," through joint tenancy (the surviving joint tenants take equally), gifts prior to death, and through trusts (the beneficiary of the trust changes after the original beneficiary dies). These procedures do not necessarily save taxes. They should be coordinated with a Will or Living Trust so that the total result is as wished. See *Will Preparation, Glossary of Will Terms, Probate,* pages 84–92.

■ **LOCATION OF ALL ASSETS** Each year millions of dollars rightfully due to owners and heirs are lost in unclaimed inheritances. Banks, savings and loan institutions, stock and bond brokerage firms and other similar companies are often simply unable to locate the rightful owners of assets they hold. After a diligent effort to locate the rightful owner, such assets are held unclaimed for the legal period of time and then revert to the state or to the institution holding them. You can avoid this situation by documenting all the appropriate information in this book and so informing your future heirs.

TWO TAX TIPS

■ **MINIMIZING TAXES** You can save money by examining your tax situation at the beginning instead of at the end of the year. You can minimize your tax liability by finding legitimate ways to invest and allocate your money rather than seeking ways around taxes. If you have a deduction you believe you are entitled to, take it. An audit does not mean that your tax return is faulty, merely that items are questioned for verification. Keep all receipts, log your automobile mileage and keep good records of your expenses and income.

■ **SAVING TAX RECORDS** You may wonder how far back income tax records must be kept in the event of a future audit. The statute of limitations requires that, under ordinary circumstances, you keep them for three years. Some experts recommend six years. In cases where the government alleges fraud or failure to file (an example is where the taxpayer fails to report more than 25% of his or her income), there is no time limit — the responsibility for disproving such a claim is the taxpayer's.

Records on real property affect the application of capital gains taxation, and all improvement records should be kept from the time the property was purchased. With all these records, your capital gains liability might well be reduced.

Keep all current tax information up-to-date in a separate file, together with previous tax information so that it is readily available if needed.

TWO CREDIT CARD TIPS

■ **WOMEN AND CREDIT CARDS** Even after many years of your using a credit card and establishing good credit in your husband's name, it can take a lot of time and aggravation to re-establish credit in your name alone, once your husband has passed on. It is a good idea to establish your personal credit record as an individual as soon as possible, as a lot of discrimination unfortunately still exists against women, particularly widows with no previous individual credit record.

■ **CREDIT CARD TELEFRAUD** Beware of phone calls offering you exotic prizes, vacations, and club memberships, who ask for your name, credit card number and expiration date. If you give this information to a stranger, you have, in effect, given away your credit card.

One California family was tracked down by private investigators for a company that had sold stock to their father over twenty years before. Since no record of the $500 in stock was found after the father's death, the family was not aware of his investment. Thanks to the company's president, who had personally sold the stock to the father and hired the investigators, the heirs were located just one week before the State was to claim the assets. The $500 in stock? It was now worth over $160,000. This family was fortunate: most heirs to unrecorded assets never know their inheritances exist.

–David S. Magee
Everything Your Heirs Need to Know About You

PART

V

GENERAL
INFORMATION

IN THIS SECTION, you will find information to help you in preparing your will. This is a complex subject, and these pages are only meant to serve as an introduction so you will be a more informed client when you see a lawyer, which I highly recommend.

Your "right to die" has taken on new meaning in the last several years, as medical technology has become more advanced. It is important to know how to retain your legal rights to refuse excessive treatments which only prolong suffering. Hospice organizations are a very good resource for support in dying, at home or in a hospital.

It is not always easy to understand the wide range of feelings associated with grief and loss; here are some ideas for coping with bereavement and getting back on the road to recovery. Lists of support groups and useful books are also included.

WILL PREPARATION

PREPARING A WILL is one of the most important responsibilities you have. Take care of it, while in good health and sound mind, early in life. If you don't already have a will, make it your first priority — regardless of your age — to have one prepared, by yourself or a lawyer.

IF YOU DIE WITHOUT A WILL

Studies show that over 50% of the people who die in the United States do not leave a will. Should you die intestate (without a will), or leave an invalid will, state laws will govern the distribution of your estate. Intestate laws will generally divide applicable assets equally among your "heirs at law," your spouse and children. Only LSTC property (Life insurance, Survivorship property — held in joint tenancy or tenancy by the entirety, property held in a Living Trust, or spouse's half of Community Property) is not governed by intestacy laws.

Settlement and distribution of an estate without a will can be cumbersome and require the filing of petitions, bonds and various notices, and securing court approval on many matters. Further, with no will, your estate might be administered by a total stranger appointed by the court. Your investments could be handled by a bank not of your choosing or others who may be unqualified or incapable of understanding your wishes or the needs of your family.

Should two parents die without a will, a court-appointed guardian (whom you might not have chosen yourself) will take custody of your children and estate. This involves the expense of hiring a lawyer, and takes time.

SOME GOOD REASONS TO LEAVE A WILL

Preparation of a will allows you to create tax strategies in the form of gifts, trusts and charitable contributions. It encourages you to assess your financial situation and see to it that your property, savings, benefits and assets will be managed wisely and distributed fairly, in accord with your wishes and good sense.

Even if you think you don't have anything, a will can cover distribution of an unexpected inheritance, or money to which your heirs would be entitled by a "wrongful death" or accident claim. With a will you can be sure that the little you do have goes to someone who appreciates its value and what it meant to you.

LEAVING SOMEONE OUT OF YOUR WILL

Some jurisdictions can overrule, modify or invalidate a will that is considered blatantly unfair (i.e., not even mentioning one's children or spouse or leaving them nothing.) A judge might consider a will objectionable to society or modify it. Be very conscious, therefore, of what you put in and what you leave out.

Will-making can and should be an open and healthy confrontation with a person's true feelings about life, death, property and the people and causes he or she loves. A well-planned estate can be a final, fitting expression of a person's philosophy of life. As Ishmael said in Moby Dick *after signing his Will: "I felt all the easier; a stone was rolled away from my heart. I survived myself."*
—New York Times

DO YOU NEED A LAWYER?

In most cases, yes! The laws concerning wills are complex and vary from state to state. You might make a will, for example, while residing in Illinois, that will ultimately involve the distribution of property in California to survivors residing in yet a third state.

Make sure all applicable laws are understood by you or your attorney, so that your estate will go to those you have designated. Even if your estate is small, the services of a lawyer are usually worthwhile.

IF YOU DECIDE TO WRITE YOUR OWN WILL

Writing your own will is far better than leaving none at all. A *holographic will*, totally handwritten, signed and dated by you can be binding and enforceable. California accepts holographic wills; not all states do. Check the laws in your state.

If you type your will or use a printed-form will, it is not holographic and must be witnessed. Laws about signing and witnessing must be followed very carefully. Check with your local State Bar Association for free pamphlets on will-making.

In all cases, keep your will simple and easy to follow, fair and workable, with anticipated taxes and expenses kept to a minimum.

UPDATING YOUR WILL

To ensure that your will is kept up-to-date, consider taking it out for review each year after you have completed your annual income tax return. Your income, assets and liabilities may be different, or a change in your personal life may trigger the need for a new beneficiary or redistribution of your estate.

Be sure to revise your will when you divorce, separate, or remarry.

LOCATION OF WILL

Make your heirs and close ones aware not only of the will's physical location, but also of its contents and provisions. File the documents in a safe deposit box, and list this information on the *Location of Records* form on page 14.

ITEMS TO CONSIDER

Here is a summary checklist of items you will need to consider in making out your will. If you are aware of these possibilities, you will be better prepared if you do use an attorney.

■ **EXECUTOR** The executor is a person named by you to carry out the terms of your will. In a more complicated will, naming a co-executor like a lawyer or a bank is sometimes helpful in avoiding expensive delays and errors. Without a named executor, a probate judge will name a person to administer your estate, someone who may or may not be aware of or sympathetic to your wishes.

■ **CHILDREN** You will want to name a legal guardian for your minor children (usually your spouse), and make provisions for the possibility of both parents dying in a common accident. Some lawyers recommend that the guardian of the person of the child and of the child's estate be different, as different talents are involved in the two tasks.

A trust may be appropriate. Without a trust, children get all of the money when they reach legal age (18 in many states); with a trust, the money is given out in designated intervals.

If your children are grown, with varying income levels, you may want more money given to those who need it more; otherwise, the money will be distributed equally.

■ **DISINHERITANCE** In most states, it is not easy to disinherit your spouse. If you are entering a new marriage, with money and children from a previous marriage, you might consider a prenuptial agreement, if you wish your children to be the main recipients of your money.

If anyone is to be excluded, name that person specifically; in most cases, the spouse and relatives are the first legal heirs, unless otherwise noted.

■ **ASSETS** Transfer of titles to all of your assets should proceed quickly to a person whom you designate in your will. Use the *Present/Future Assets* form on page 64 to list the value of all your assets, such as real estate, pension plans, money market funds, life insurance etc., and who holds title to each, the policy number, face amount, cash value and outstanding loans.

■ **TAXES** Under the "marital deduction" you may leave an unlimited amount of wealth (property, life insurance, and other assets) to your spouse free of federal estate taxes. But after both spouses are gone, and assets are to pass to the children or others, estate taxes can be enormous, and should be planned for in the form of trusts or gifts. A certain amount can be taken as a deduction from your "taxable estate" when you are leaving it to persons other than your spouse. Depending on whether your estate exceeds current legal exemption figures, you may consider more complex tax-saving devices such as private annuities, installment sales, family corporations, partnerships, or others. For example, a "bypass trust" may leave use of the money to the surviving spouse, but pass it tax-free to the children later.

■ **GIFTS** You can use gift money to lower your taxable estate. A certain annual amount is allowable by law.

■ **TRUSTS** A trust allows you to perpetuate your wishes over a period of time and avoid overpayment of taxes. If you name a trustee, that person or trust company can manage your property and other assets in accordance with your desires as specified in the trust document. There are too many trusts to consider in any detail or even to list in this work. The same types of trusts are often called by different names. There are trusts set up during the benefactor's lifetime (Living Trusts, also called Inter Vivos Trusts, which can be revocable or irrevocable), and trusts established in a will (called Testamentary or Probate Trust). Under those broad outlines, there are tax savings trusts which could be established either before death or in a will, such as a Bypass (also called an Exemption Trust, which allows funds to be used for a survivor's benefit, but not to be taxed to the survivor on his/her death). There are Q-TIP Trusts for spouses and Generation-skipping Trusts for grandchildren and later generations; there are Life Insurance Trusts. All of these, in some circumstances, can be used to save death taxes. Any step taken to avoid taxes must be drafted to take advantage of then-current tax laws.

■ **REVOCABLE LIVING TRUSTS** Revocable Living Trusts have become very popular in recent years and have been heavily promoted. In come cases, they have even been promoted by door-to-door sales. A Revocable Living Trust, if properly set up and maintained, can avoid probate. The tax consequences of a properly drafted will and a probate and a properly drafted Revocable Living Trust are nearly the same. In other words, although there may be tax savings gained through the trusts, those same tax savings may be gained through a will. Either is a clear improvement on intestacy. The cost may be less than probate, but i some cases exceeds the cost of probate. Costs of probate may be exaggerated (e.g., executor-heirs often work for nothing; they may inherit the property tax-free, but would pay income taxes on the executor's fees).

Transfers must be made to the trust during the trustor's lifetime. There are expenses in that procedure and further expenses when transfers must be made by the trustee to the new beneficiaries on the death of the trustor. There can be other ongoing expenses, as there can be complications caused by having property in a Revocable Living Trust. New property acquired must be properly titled or will not conform with the originally intended distribution on death. A will must accompany a Revocable Living Trust because no matter how conscientious the trustor, some property (e.g., funds recovered out of the accident in which the trustor died) will not be placed in the trust. The privacy which allegedly accompanies a Revocable Living Trust may be an illusion (stockbrokers and others businesses titling assets may require a copy of the trust before they will put title in the trust name), or may be a disadvantage (misappropriation can more easily happen where there is privacy). Nevertheless, depending on the individual circumstances, a Revocable Living Trust should be considered in connection with an estate plan.

■ **LIFE INSURANCE** You will generally have named a beneficiary in your policy, so this does not need to be mentioned in your will. Consider taking out more life insurance if you discover that the amount of your estate after taxes is not enough to cover the needs of your heirs.

If you name your trust as beneficiary of your life insurance, it can be paid out under the terms of the trust, and allow the trustee to determine the amounts given to each beneficiary according to their needs at the time.

■ **CHARITABLE CONTRIBUTIONS** Mention any money you wish to leave to charity or any other type of organization or institution, such as a university or hospital. A Charitable Remainder Intent Gift enables you to take a tax deduction now for the present value of a gift you will not pay until after you die. But if you use this tax break, you cannot change your mind about it later.

■ **BURIAL ARRANGEMENTS** Many people write these requests into their will, but since the will is often not read until after the burial takes place, it is wiser to call these provisions to the attention of the appropriate person in advance. Use the forms on pages 17 and 19 to outline your desires, and make your arrangements now.

GLOSSARY OF WILL TERMS

ADMINISTRATOR A person or institution appointed by the court to administer the estate of a decedent (deceased person). The duties are the same as an executor's but an executor is named by the decedent in a will.

ANNUITY A periodic payment (monthly, quarterly, etc.) of a fixed sum of money for a set period of time.

BENEFICIARY The recipient of a benefit from a will, a trust, or a life insurance policy.

BEQUEATH To leave something to someone by will. Historically, it referred only to personal property, whereas the word "devise" referred to real property. "Bequeath," "devise," and "give" are now used interchangeably with reference to wills.

CODICIL A supplement that changes the provisions of a will. A formal change to a will that is admissible in probate.

COMMUNITY PROPERTY Property belonging equally to husband and wife. Only exists in "community property" states. Earnings of either spouse during their marriage, or by agreement that it be held as community property. Its opposite is "separate property," owned by either a husband or wife but not both, and usually acquired before this marriage or by individual gift or inheritance during the marriage and sometimes by agreement between the husband and wife.

CONTINGENT BENEFICIARY A beneficiary who only receives the gift if the contingency occurs. For example, "I give to my friend Benny $1000 but only (1) if he survives me, and (2) if he is married to Jane at the time of my death."

CORPUS The principal of an estate or a trust.

CURTESY The right of a surviving husband in his deceased wife's estate. Called ELECTIVE SHARE in some states. (See DOWER.) Only recognized in some states.

CUSTODIAN One who holds something, who has the care and possession of a thing, such as "the bank is the custodian of the will." A person who has other duties, such as a trustee, may also have custody of documents, property, etc., but the term custodian alone does not imply duties beyond caretaking.

DECEDENT A deceased person.

DEVISE See BEQUEATH.

DOMICILE One's permanent home. The place to which an absent person intends to return. While residence and domicile are usually the same, a person may reside for a long time away from his domicile; for instance, military personnel or people on job assignments. It is legal (as opposed to physical) "residence" and may be important in determining which jurisdiction will cover the handling and distribution of the estate. It is a factual question, and such things as place of voting, bank accounts, home ownership, etc. are considered.

DONEE One receiving a gift.

DONOR One making a gift.

DOWER The right a surviving wife has in her deceased husband's estate. Called ELECTIVE SHARE in some states. (See CURTESY.) Only recognized in some states.

ELECTIVE SHARE/ELECTION The right of a surviving spouse to take a portion of the deceased spouse's net probate estate (also called FORCED SHARE). The surviving spouse is entitled to at least this amount, but may be put to "an election." A decedent's will could provide: "My spouse may have income from all my property for life after which the property will go to my children." The spouse could elect to accept that gift or refuse it and take the "elective share" outright.

ESTATE A deceased person's accumulations or worldly possessions, both real and personal; the ownership or interest that someone has in real or personal property.

ESTATE TAX Usually, the federal tax levied on the estate of a deceased person. (See INHERITANCE TAX.) An estate tax and an inheritance tax are different: estate tax is computed on the decedent's estate, inheritance tax is computed on the beneficiary's inheritance. The federal government only has an estate tax. Many states have inheritance taxes. Although both taxes may be reduced by marital or charitable gifts, the inheritance tax depends much more than the estate tax on who inherits. Different rates may apply, for instance, to minor children, adult children, and non-relatives.

EUTHANASIA Causing death without pain, to end suffering, for reasons considered to be merciful.

EXECUTOR A person or institution appointed by the deceased in a will, to carry out the terms of the will. If the will is to be probated, the executor sees that the will is put before the court and that the court authorizes him to handle the probate. An executor reports to the court.

FIDUCIARY A trustee or other person who manages property and exercises rights for a beneficiary. A fiduciary is held to a higher degree of care and integrity in dealing with the beneficiary than is a non-fiduciary.

FORCED SHARE See ELECTIVE SHARE.

GUARDIAN One who has legal care and control over the property or person of a minor or incompetent person. A will may nominate a guardian to be appointed by a court, or a guardian may be appointed in special proceedings by a court whenever necessary.

HEIR Technically, a person receiving a share of an intestate estate under the laws of inheritance. Often used to describe one who receives property from an estate, with or without a will.

INHERITANCE TAX The state tax that heirs, survivors, or beneficiaries must pay when they receive a deceased person's property. (See ESTATE TAX.) Inheritance tax is computed only on the beneficiary's share of the total estate.

INTESTATE When one dies without a valid will.

INTESTACY PROPERTY Property of a person who dies without a will, which will be distributed to heirs according to state laws of intestacy.

IRREVOCABLE Cannot be revoked, cancelled, changed or amended. For example, an "irrevocable trust."

JOINT TENANCY Joint tenants, by definition, own equal percentages, i.e., if there are five joint tenants, each has a 20% interest. The term "joint tenancy" generally implies the right of survivorship; if that is not desired, a different form of ownership should be used. JOINT TENANCY WITH RIGHT OF SURVIVORSHIP means holding title to property in such a way that when one person dies, his or her share automatically goes to the surviving joint tenant(s), and is not subject to the laws of intestacy and is not dependent on the provisions of the deceased person's will.

LAWS OF INTESTACY State laws that determine who receives the property of a deceased person with no will, or a wholly or partially invalid will. There can be "partial intestacy" if all of the decedent's property is not disposed of by will.

LEGACY Historically, a gift of personal property made in a will. A "bequest" historically was a gift of real property in a will.

LETTERS OF ADMINISTRATION A certificate issued by the court qualifying and authorizing the administrator to administer the estate.

LETTERS TESTAMENTARY A certificate issued by the Probate Court authorizing the executor to probate a deceased's estate.

LIFE ESTATE Property ownership limited to the life of the owner, and in rare instances, to the life of some other named person.

LIFE INSURANCE TRUST A trust established during the life of the insured person which holds the life insurance policy(ies) and collects on its proceeds on the death of the insured, and distributes them according to the trust's terms.

LIVING TRUST A trust set up while you are still alive.

LIVING WILL A written statement of your desires regarding how much medical treatment you want in the event of a terminal illness.

MARITAL DEDUCTION Property that qualifies passes directly to the spouse and is not subject to federal estate or gift taxes. Some states have inheritance taxes, which vary as to the allowable marital deduction.

MARITAL TRUST A trust that complies with IRS requirements so that any deposit into the trust qualifies for the marital deduction.

PERSONAL PROPERTY Any property that is not real estate. Moveable property. Can be tangible (i.e., antiques) or intangible (i.e., a debt).

POUR-OVER WILL A will that transfers ("pours over") a portion of all of an estate into an existing or living trust.

POWER OF APPOINTMENT A power conferred on one through a will or other appropriate document appointing that person to determine who will receive property or income after certain interests terminate. For example, a husband's will might appoint his wife to determine who receives the balance of his estate at her subsequent death.

POWER OF ATTORNEY A writing by which a person (called the "principal") authorizes another person (called the "attorney-in-fact") to act on his or her behalf. It can be limited to certain issues or can be a general attorney-in-fact which would pertain to all matters. Especially important when designated to make health care decisions in the event of an accident or terminal illness.

PRIMARY BENEFICIARY The person who will receive property from a will or trust unless other circumstances occur. For instance, "To my son Benny, if he is living at the time of my death, otherwise to his daughter Benecia."

PROBATE The process of settling an estate and transferring property to beneficiaries or heirs under the supervision of Probate Court. *(See page 92.)* If there is a will, its validity will be established in probate proceedings.

PROBATE ESTATE Property of the deceased that is subject to probate laws. Does not include certain property not subject to probate, such as property held in joint tenancy with right of survivorship, or property payable to a named beneficiary such as life insurance, retirement benefits, etc.

Q Tip Trust *Q*ualified *T*erminal *I*nterest *P*roperty Trust. A trust which qualifies under IRS rules may obtain the marital deduction even if the interest left to the spouse is "terminable." Previously, property left to the surviving spouse could be left to anyone he/she chose. Now, you may leave your spouse income from a property for life, and also state where the property should go after your spouse dies.

Real Property Land, fixed improvements (structures, fences, paving, etc.) and growing things thereon; as contrasted to Personal Property.

Residue The amount left in a decedent's estate after payment of debts, taxes and other expenses, and after distribution of gifts which are specifically set forth. For instance, "I leave my stamp collection to Joe, $1000 to Harry, and the rest, residue, and remainder to my son Benny."

Revocable Subject to being cancelled, changed, amended, revoked or modified.

Secondary Beneficiary The beneficiary who would take over of the primary beneficiary were disqualified.

Settlor The person who establishes, and usually funds, a trust.

Spouse One's husband or wife.

Sprinkling Trust A trust under which the trustee has the discretion to decide how much of the trust may be given to two or more beneficiaries. The trust proceeds may be "sprinkled" between various beneficiaries. The most needy beneficiary may get the most money and/or there may be tax benefits by giving money to beneficiaries in the lowest tax brackets.

Surrogate In a broad sense, a person who is substituted or appointed to act for another. Some states refer to probate court as surrogate's court.

Tenancy in Common Two or more people who hold property in common; may own unequal percentages. It does not carry the right of survivorship, so when one dies, he may leave his share to whomever he names in his will. Under the laws of intestacy, that share will not go automatically to the other owners.

Tenant Normally thought of as one who rents or leases real property from the owner. Technically, means anyone in possession of real property.

Testamentary Trust Any trust established in one's will.

Testate One who has made a will, or who dies leaving a will, is described as being testate (opposite of intestate); a testator.

Title Ownership of property (most often, real property).

Trust A legal device wherein a settlor transfers property of any type to a trustee to hold, manage, or distribute it, as instructed by the trust.

Trustee The person or institution who holds trust property, manages it and distributes it to the beneficiaries, in accordance with the terms of the trust.

Will A legal document directing disbursement of one's property after death.

PROBATE

SIMPLY PUT, probate is the process of settling the estate of a deceased person under the supervision of a probate court, and accomplishing the transfer of his or her property to heirs or beneficiaries.

Depending on the size and complexity of an estate, going through probate is costly and can cause lengthy delays in the clearing of an estate. Probate can be avoided in many cases by setting up a Living Trust. Life insurance, property held in joint tenancy, and community property belonging to your spouse are not subject to probate.

Once a death occurs, titles to all your property must be transferred to others. The probate court communicates to the appropriate persons or agencies that you had clear title to the property and that the transfer to another is authorized and lawful. For example, the Department of Motor Vehicles is notified regarding transfer of registration on your car, your stockbroker for transfer of title to your stocks, etc.

DISADVANTAGES OF PROBATE

There are entire books on how to avoid probate. You will need good professional advice to determine what is best for you. Some of the disadvantages of a probated estate are:

■ **TIME** A simple estate often takes nine months to one year to probate. Complex estates can take several years.

■ **COST** Probate adds lawyers' and executors' fees to expenses your heirs already face.

■ **PUBLICITY** With probate, public notice is required in newspapers advising of your death, who the executor is, and when claims can be filed.

All probate court records are public as well, and are available to anyone.

ADVANTAGES OF PROBATE

While the major disadvantages of going through probate are time and cost, there are several advantages:

■ **CLEAR TITLE** Cars, homes, boats, bank accounts, and other assets that were in your name alone are clearly transferred to your heirs or beneficiaries exactly as instructed in your will. This title-clearing function can be important in avoiding squabbles or lawsuits over who was the rightful heir.

■ **EXECUTION** The probate court oversees the entire process of the administration of your will. Your will is executed to the letter and the chances of disputes minimized.

■ **CREDITORS** With probate, creditors have a limited period of time to make financial demands on your heirs, usually 60 to 120 days after certain preliminary probate procedures have been completed. Without probate (or similar procedures allowed sometimes with a living trust), they can make claims until the normal statute of limitations runs out, which can be many years. This is particularly important for people in a business which might subject them to claims arising from future events, such as lawyers, doctors, contractors, etc.

As you can see, it is extremely important to do some advance planning in the titling of your property, trusts, wills and other related matters. Financial consequences for survivors can be significant, while the orderly transfer of assets will be appreciated all the more by your heirs.

DONATION OF BODY OR ORGANS

THE BEQUEATHAL of a body or organs for anatomical study or transplant is a gift to those who benefit from this research. Kidneys, heart, lungs, skin and corneas have all been successfully transplanted into living persons in need of new organs. But you must choose between a body or part donation, as most medical schools will not accept a body for study if parts are missing. While most schools continue to have urgent need, an increasing number are amply supplied and may or may not accept bequeathals at any given time. It is therefore important to have an alternative plan available, either through a memorial society or funeral home.

Call the anatomy department at the medical school nearest you for specific information about their needs and requirements for bequeathal, and the possibility of donating specific organs for transplant or study, and if this is your wish, register your desire with that school so that your name is on file with them.

At the time of death, survivors should contact the school to have the body delivered directly there. Most schools will pay transportation expenses within a certain distance, usually fifty miles. The family may consider delivering the body themselves, on a stretcher or simply wrapped in a blanket. Legally, the physician in charge must sign a death certificate which is then taken to the county Board of Health where a transportation permit is issued. If a common carrier is used, such as Amtrak or an airline, the services of a funeral director will be required.

A memorial service may then be held without the body of the deceased present. The school will generally take care of disposing of the remains following the useful educational life of the body, or cremated ashes may be returned to survivors for burial or scattering; but this may be two or three years later.

UNIFORM ANATOMICAL GIFT ACT

This law is in effect in all 50 states, and allows you to document your desire to donate your body or organs for educational purposes. Write to the U.S. Department of Health and Human Services, Washington, DC 20201, and request publication No. (NIH) 79-776, and you will receive a pamphlet called "How to Donate Your Body or Its Organs." This will include a Uniform Donor Card. It is recommended that you carry this card with you at all times in case you become the victim of an accidental death, since speed of delivery is critical for transplant of organs. As always, be sure to inform those who should know about your wish (and put it in writing), as the Uniform Donor Card can be negated if next of kin is opposed.

STATE OF CALIFORNIA
DMV
DEPARTMENT OF MOTOR VEHICLES
A Public Service Agency

Pursuant to the Uniform Anatomical Gift Act.
I hereby elect upon my death the following option(s):

A __ To donate any organ or parts

B __ To donate a pacemaker (date implanted _____)

C __ To donate parts or organs listed _____
_____

D __ To not donate any organs, parts or pacemaker.

_____
SIGNATURE   DATE

DL 290 (REV 5/92)

HOSPICE

HOSPICE ORGANIZATIONS offer specialized health care programs for the terminally ill. In the United States, they mostly provide home care support, including a supervising doctor, a nurse who monitors day-to-day care, a counselor such as a social worker or pastor, and volunteers to assist and provide respite care for the family and others when needed. You may retain your own doctor, and use your local hospice as a resource for whatever additional support you and your loved ones might need, whether medical, practical or emotional. Most hospice organizations offer 24-hours-a-day, 7-days-a-week service, either in the home or hospital.

More and more insurance carriers are recognizing hospice as a less expensive, as well as more personal approach to treating the terminally ill.

Hospice-assisted home care can help ease the cost of hospital care, and also allow the dying patient the comfort of being at home and in the company of family and loved ones during this critical time.

You can find out if there's a hospice program in your area by contacting your county health department or home health service, a hospital social worker or chaplain, or the National Hospice Organization.

NATIONAL HOSPICE ORGANIZATION
1901 N. Moore Street, Suite 901
Arlington, VA 22209   (703) 243-5900

NHO is a national coordinating body for hospice organizations. It sponsors national and regional meetings, develops standards of care, provides educational materials and a newsletter, and advocates hospice coverage by governmental and private insurance programs.

RIGHT TO DIE

EVERY SINGLE DAY in homes, hospitals, and nursing homes across the country, highly personal, profound "life and death" decisions are being made, not alone by the dying patient and loved ones, but together with attending physicians, under the provisions of widely varying state laws about the right to die, and an individual doctor's or institution's philosophy and interpretation of that law.

At home, you have more control over how your dying is handled; under the care of an institution, your rights are generally more restricted. Because the law strictly "protects" the patient, institutions take great care to protect themselves from the threat of lawsuits. If the patient's wishes are not known (not written), or cannot be known (as with infants, the comatose, severely disabled, or accident and trauma victims), those rights default back to the prevailing legal, medical, ethical philosophy of the family, doctors and institution charged with the patient's care.

In dire circumstances, the right to die question basically contains two aspects, which may be defined as the difference between *active* and *passive euthanasia*. Declining treatment or "pulling the plug" on life support systems that are keeping someone alive artificially are considered passive acts. In most American states, laws exist which allow you to declare, preferably in writing using the Living Will and/or Durable Power of Attorney, your wish that your life not be prolonged artificially; under appropriate conditions, this choice may be recognized as merciful even by the Catholic church. You can legally refuse excessive treatment in most states. This includes respirators, nutrition and hydration, though withholding food and hydration is more subject to a doctor's personal medical and ethical opinion.

The second, more controversial aspect involves the notion of active euthanasia, that is, actively doing something known to cause death. Also called self-deliverance (if you do it yourself), assisted suicide (if someone else does it), or physician assisted aid-in-dying (if your doctor provides and administers the means); this is not yet legal in any state.

LIVING WILL
(Passive Euthanasia)

The Living Will is a written directive to your physician wherein you can state in writing how you want to be treated if at any time you should become unable to make your own decisions on important health care matters. This includes having extreme treatments or artificial life support withheld, or, on the other hand, your wish to receive maximum treatment. Because so many people in modern Western society die in hospitals, dying often involves a decision to refuse some medical procedure that could prolong the process. If you want to retain your right to control how these decisions get made, it will require planning and forethought, and increasingly important, documentation.

Get your state's version of the Living Will. Sign it, and have it witnessed. These forms may be obtained from your State Medical Association, your attorney, or sometimes your hospital. This written directive may or may not be enforceable in your state, but as a signed "release" it will at least be a valuable factor in your doctor's thinking, and provide some protection to the doctor from possible lawsuits by relatives after your death.

Discuss this document with your physician, family, and lawyer, and distribute signed, witnessed copies to them.

DURABLE POWER OF ATTORNEY FOR HEALTH CARE
(Passive Euthanasia)

This form is more potent and legally binding than the Living Will. In different versions, it is available in all fifty American states from your State Medical Association, attorney, physician or hospital. The significant difference from the Living Will is that using the *Durable Power of Attorney for Health Care* form allows you to name a person to act on your behalf to carry out your wishes. Should you become incapacitated, for any reason, your doctor will turn first to your next of kin. If you anticipate any dissent in your family, a surrogate you name in this document becomes the "attorney-in-fact" and will have an overriding say. You should be aware, however, that this document, according to most current state laws, provides only for the withholding of treatment; it does not cover the extraordinary but all too common case where the patient wishes active deliverance.

HEMLOCK SOCIETY
(Active Euthanasia)

The Hemlock Society believes that a person who is terminally ill and suffering should legally be allowed to end his or her life, and if necessary, get help in doing so, ideally from a physician. Such help is not yet lawful. However, more and more prosecutors are finding it difficult to obtain convictions in "mercy killing" cases, and there is indeed a growing reluctance to indict at all.

Hemlock Society founder Derek Humphry's book *Final Exit* includes specific prescriptions for overdosing and other methods to help the dying end their own lives. This book has been a bestseller, demonstrating the depth of interest in the issue and the need to address it socially, legally and morally. But as of this writing, active physician aid-in-dying ("assisted suicide") remains illegal in every state in the country, and still carries significant personal and professional risk for those who provide it. Publishing specific information is not considered a crime (hence the existence of the book), but counseling someone and procuring the medication is; being there at the time of death is not illegal, but touching the person in the act (giving injections, holding spoons up to mouth) creates potential liability.

DEATH WITH DIGNITY ACT
(Active Euthanasia)

The California Death with Dignity Act was written and placed on the November 1992 voter's ballot by Californians Against Human Suffering, a group whose goals parallel those of the Hemlock Society; specifically, to change state right-to-die laws to accommodate individual choice in this deeply personal matter. To change law requires proceeding one step at a time. Therefore, the Act addressed only terminally ill patients whose wishes can be known, and allowed only for physician assisted aid-in-dying. It did not provide for the severely handicapped, infants and children, and others unable to express their own desires and contained many safeguards against possible abuse of the right. Only the terminally ill patient would decide when the time for aid-in-dying has arrived, and no one but a doctor would legally be allowed to administer such aid. The Act was voted down in a close race, indicating the deep ambivalence people feel about providing legal sanctions for ending a life.

PHYSICIAN ASSISTED AID-IN-DYING
(Active Euthanasia)

Doctor Jack Kevorkian, who practices in Michigan, has taken the matter further: he has helped people to die who cannot officially be classified as "terminally ill." On June 4, 1990, he helped a woman in the early stages of Alzheimer's disease, a degenerative disease of the brain, end her own life before her symptoms became more serious. He then talked freely about it in the New York *Times,* and some newspapers began referring to him as "the suicide doctor." This action brought the matter before the public in an unprecedented manner and drew both praise and criticism. Criticism focused on the possible extension of this kind of act: should doctors be providing prescriptions for death to anyone who asks for it: teenage suicide candidates, the depressed, the medically indigent? Others support Dr. Kevorkian's view that right-to-die laws should be broad enough to provide freedom of choice for everyone, especially those who face a future of more and more inactivity, suffering, and physical and mental deterioration: Alzheimer's disease victims, paraplegics, brain-damaged infants. See *Books for Further Reading*, page 104, for information on Dr. Kevorkian's own book on this matter.

THE DEBATE OVER EUTHANASIA

The stated social commitment of the physician is to sustain life, and to relieve suffering. But what happens when these are not one and the same, when to relieve suffering means not sustaining life? The National Hospice Organization has opposed the Death with Dignity Act and the concept of legal physician aid-in-dying for several reasons. Quality of life, personal dignity, self-determination, and choice are the stated missions of both Hospice and Hemlock, but Hospice feels that choosing death while you are still alive,

denies the life that is still going on. Hospice has found that those who persist, who do not opt to prematurely end their lives, often discover unforeseen benefits: opportunities for patient and family to come to terms with death, to have new spiritual insights, and unanticipated peace at the end of life. The time of dying may be looked upon as sacred and not to be rushed through in a desire to avoid perceived pain.

Dr. Cecily Saunders, founder of the Hospice movement, believes that death will arrive in its own time anyway, and can happen without excessive pain because drugs available these days can control pain so well. Others would argue that drugs cannot eliminate all pain, particularly the mental and emotional pain that comes with the conscious knowledge that to continue living will mean only further deterioration.

Dr. Ira Byock, medical director of Mountain West Hospice in Missoula, Montana, and a member of the ethics committee of NHO, makes a stirring plea against providing a legal basis for active euthanasia. What he calls the "slippery slope" of setting this kind of legal precedent, he feels, opens a door for weary doctors to choose assisted suicide as a primary means of handling the nation's terminally ill and medically indigent. It is less expensive to provide easy death than the palliative, life-sustaining care which Hospice would like to see made more readily available. He also feels that asking doctors to take active roles in providing death to the dying is a critical compromise to the medical profession's social role as guardian and enhancer of life.

That there is a need for legal support of everyone's right to die is a more and more commonly held public perception. There are any number of people for whom an early, intentional death is a legitimate response to their ill condition and suffering. Dr. Byock proposes that political energies be directed first, ideally, to providing the means for genuine access to more comprehensive health care reform and higher quality hospice and palliative care. Relief from suffering should be available to all who need it, including compassionate support and legal choices which respect the wide variety of individual preferences as to how one's life should end.

CHANGING TIMES

In February of 1993, the Netherlands became the first Western nation to provide guidelines for doctors to legally carry out mercy killings on patients who are incurably ill. The vote by parliament endorsed procedures already being followed by many members of the medical community. The new law, scheduled to take effect in 1994, included a detailed 28-point checklist which must be followed by doctors, proving that the patient is terminally ill, suffers unbearable pain and wishes to die. The patient must be in a clear state of mind and ask repeatedly to die. The request cannot come from family or friends.

The emotional Dutch debate drew a clear distinction between a doctor who withdraws treatment and one who actively ends a life. The removal of life support systems in futile cases remains an acceptable practice in the Netherlands and other European countries, as well as in some U.S. states, including California. The new law, it is hoped, will bring the issue of mercy killing more into the open so that it can be properly regulated. The guidelines, also called "carefulness requirements," make it clear that requests to die cannot be made on impulse or be based on

temporary depression, a full range of alternatives and information on the patient's condition must have been presented, and the patient must "experience his or her suffering as perpetual, unbearable and hopeless."

This law is limited in that it only provides for coherent, terminally ill individuals, and does not address the coma victim, damaged infants, the severely handicapped or others unable to speak for themselves. The moral problem of how to manage the living and dying of these patients will still have to be handled privately and individually, with no easy solution readily available from governments or courts of law.

UNDERSTANDING GRIEF AND LOSS

by Stephen Jamison Ph.D.

GRIEF IS THE TERM given to the thoughts, emotions, physical symptoms, and behaviors that result from a major loss. What each of us defines as loss varies. Some reserve the term for the death of one significant in their lives. Others include serious changes in relationships, while still others recognize their right to grieve any great change due to job loss, retirement, relocation, or loss of a physical ability. One's emotional pain from divorce can feel as real as another's response to a significant death.

What grief shows is that our connections and love for others are not easily severed. Viewed like this, grief is how we emotionally honor the depth of a union between ourselves and someone else.

HOW IT FEELS

Researchers have found that grief sensations occur in waves that last from twenty minutes to an hour, and include sobbing, crying, need for sighing, tightness in throat and chest, shortness of breath, lack of energy, tension, and an empty feeling in the abdomen. This set of feelings has been called pangs of grief, and may begin shortly after the loss — a few hours to days — and last from a few days to weeks. Over time, they occur less often, and eventually are expressed only when there is an anniversary or other reminder of the loss. When these symptoms don't begin immediately, we may feel numb or in shock.

Grief can be experienced physically, emotionally, cognitively, and behaviorally. All four are usually present and they change during the grieving process.

HOW LONG IT LASTS

Researchers agree that there are three to four phases of grief:

■ shock or denial;

■ protest, despair, anger, or pining;

■ depression, withdrawal, or disorganization;

■ recovery or acceptance.

There is no set time period for each stage, but the first phase usually wears off within two weeks, while the entire grieving process may take two years or longer. Importantly, the process should be seen as a wheel on which we move from one stage to the next and back again. We may think we have recovered only to succumb again to earlier symptoms.

Grief can be a preoccupying wound that takes time and attention to heal. Emotional pain is not constant, but can seem so if we try to suppress our feelings. It cannot be ignored, but will be felt until we process it and reach closure. Process is a good way to look at it. Though we never stop caring, we take the raw material of our loss and gradually shape it into something we can live with. In this way, we don't just recover; we are transformed.

THE VALUE OF SOLITUDE

On the way to recovering, spend time by yourself. Healing requires reflection, and this means being alone. Whatever you choose to do — meditating, reading, listening to music or self-help tapes, writing letters or a journal, drawing or painting, exercising, gardening, vacationing, or cleaning — solitude gives you a chance to be alone with your thoughts. What you do is secondary to the inner dialog that accompanies what you do.

TIPS FOR GRIEF RECOVERY

1 Allow yourself to move in and out of pain naturally. Confronting grief shortens its duration. Be open to the grieving process; recognize the range and intensity of your feelings and talk or cry as much as necessary.

2 There's no need to control or reshape your emotions out of fear that you might hurt other survivors, lose control, be misunderstood, or seen by others as vulnerable.

3 Self support is a way of self love. Give freely to yourself:

■ become aware of and honor your need for physical comfort;

■ respect your emotions and your desire to express them;

■ trust and follow your inner voice.

4 Know that grief will change you whether or not you want change, and whether or not you express your emotions. You cannot prevent change by fighting your feelings. Change is a part of surviving loss.

5 Grief ends when you can finally let go of the intense connection you have with what you have lost. This is not the same as the end of love. Your love may never die, but the pain of loss can eventually dissolve.

6 Your grief is special. Others are not always right or do not necessarily know the best way to support you. You might do well to ignore them if they:

■ tell you that talking about your feelings doesn't do you any good;

■ counsel you not to be weak or not to express your pain or sadness;

■ urge you to think of others who are worse off;

■ see your sadness or despair as "wallowing" or a "waste of time";

■ urge you to "focus on tomorrow and forget the past."

7 Solitude is often appropriate, but when it becomes "withdrawing," reach out to others. Think about what family members, friends, or organizations might be sources of support for you.

8 We each need to mourn in ways and for periods of time that feel right for us. Funerals or memorials are only one way, and your mourning does not have to end when a funeral ends. Use your own emotional timetable.

9 Create your own personally meaningful ceremonies, celebrations and ritual activities. Use your creative spirit to help you through the grieving process. You might consider making your own mourning quilt or expressing your emotions visually by painting or drawing, verbally through poems or letters, musically through songs, or physically through some form of movement or a pilgrimage to a special place.

SUPPORT GROUPS

PEER SUPPORT groups can be of great help in dealing constructively with grief or loss. Such groups exist for widows, people who have lost newborns, infants or older children, and victims of terminal diseases. Other organizations provide research, information, and education, and may be found in nearly every town and city across the country.

Taking positive action in response to an illness or death, like joining a group and working with others in similar situations, is often the first step in the healing process.

See page 99 for advice on understanding and coping with grief and loss.

If you do not wish to join a group in person, pamphlets for the bereaved are available from many of the groups listed here. Remember that Hospice is a valuable source for support *(see page 94)*. *Books for Further Reading (page 104)* lists useful reading material.

GRIEF AND HEALING

Center for Attitudinal Healing
19 Main Street
Tiburon, CA 94920
(415) 435-5022

Supplements traditional health care through regular group meetings in which children, youth, and adults faced with life-threatening illness can actively participate in attitudinal healing, a process of letting go of painful, fearful attitudes. Its focus is on quality living no matter the circumstances. Groups are for people of any age, those with long-term illnesses or disabilities, and their caregivers. Non-sectarian spiritual and emotional support.

Centering Corporation
1531 Saddle Creek Road
Omaha, NE 68104
(402) 553-1200
FAX (402) 553-0507

A grief resource center, founded in 1977, nonprofit, tax-exempt. Publishes books and provides workshops, newsletter, and booklets on patient education for children, and for siblings and parents bereaved through divorce, miscarriage, newborn death, death of older children or grandparents. Write for catalog which lists their publications as well as over a hundred books by other publishers on the subjects of grief and coping.

Compassionate Friends
PO Box 3696
Oak Brook, IL 60522-3696
(708) 990-0010

Self-help organization offering support and understanding to bereaved parents and siblings of children who died. Call national office number listed above for information on local chapters in your area.

Foundation of Thanatology
630 West 168th Street
New York, NY 10032
(212) 928-2066

Extensive library, symposia on psychological aspects of dying, and reactions to death, loss and grief. Scientific and theoretical emphasis.

Grief Education Institute
1780 S. Bellaire Street
Denver, CO 80222
(303) 758-6048

Founded by bereaved parents, provides information on grief and bereavement, support groups, and facilitator training for those who wish to lead their own workshops.

HUMOR Project
110 Spring Street
Saratoga Springs, NY 12866
(518) 587-8770

Since 1977, The HUMOR Project has provided services, programs and resources that focus on the positive power of humor and creativity to help improve the quality of life for individuals, groups and organizations. Services include conferences, workshops, a speakers bureau and a mail-order catalog of books, tapes and videos to help tap the power of humor and creativity to heal and "get more mileage and smileage out of your life and work."

International THEOS Foundation
(They Help Each Other Spiritually)
1301 Clark Building
717 Liberty Avenue
Pittsburgh, PA 15222
(412) 471-7779

Self-help groups for widowed women. Publishes quarterly newsletter, "The Communicator." Has almost one hundred chapters throughout United States and Canada. Monthly meetings.

Living-Dying Project
PO Box 357
Fairfax, CA 94978
(415) 456-3357

National educational resource for information on living and dying; provides speakers and brochures. Local social services such as support groups for children whose parents have life-threatening illnesses, occasional workshops on using grief as a transformative power, and volunteers who offer one-to-one support during a period of grieving or dying.

AIDS AND CANCER

American Cancer Society
1180 Avenue of the Americas
New York, NY 10036
(212) 382-2169

Through regional and local groups, provides sick room equipment for home use, reference material for doctors, support services. National program of research and education.

Candlelighters Childhood Cancer Foundation
7910 Woodmont Avenue
Suite 460
Bethesda, MD 20814
(301) 657-8401; (800) 366-2223

Support groups for families of children with cancer. Four hundred member groups worldwide in 1992. Publishes quarterly newsletters for youth and one for parents.

Commonweal Cancer Project
PO Box 316
Bolinas, CA 94924
(415) 868-0970
FAX (415) 868-2230

Among other educational and research functions, Commonweal offers week-long residential workshops each year for people with cancer and their family members or close friends. The goals of the program are to reduce the stress of cancer, provide mutual support, and create a learning environment in which options in lifestyle change and choice in cancer therapies can be explored. Includes sessions on gentle yoga, progressive deep relaxation, meditation, imagery, art, poetry, and psychosocial support.

The Commonweal Cancer Project seeks to raise the level of professional and public discourse about complementary cancer therapies. Informed patients and their physicians can learn to integrate the best of conventional cancer therapies with alternative and adjunctive methods. Publications include books and videotapes on unconventional cancer treatments, varieties of integral cancer therapy and choice in cancer.

National AIDS Hotline
(800) 342-2437

The person on the other end of this 800 Hotline number is there to answer your questions about AIDS, provide brochures, pamphlets or posters, and make referrals for whatever services you might need, including doctors, support groups, counseling and testing.

SHANTI Project
525 Howard Street
San Francisco, CA 94105
(415) 777-2273

Peer counseling support groups
for AIDS patients and their
caregivers in the San Francisco
Bay Area. Sets up "volunteer
matches" which provide
emotional and practical help at
home. Activities programs of
cultural and social events.
Medical transportation vans.

St. Francis Center
1768 Church Street NW
Washington, DC 20036
(202) 363-8500

A nonprofit, nonsectarian
organization providing
counseling for persons facing a
life-threatening illness.
Conducts educational programs
on death and dying. Brochures
available on request; send
SASE with 52¢ postage.

RIGHT TO DIE

Choice in Dying
200 Varick Street 10th Floor
New York, NY 10014
(212) 366-5540

Concern for Dying and the
Society for the Right to Die have
merged to form this new group
which distributes Living Wills

and other documents which the
state requires for retaining your
legal right to choice in dying.
Publishes newsletters and other
educational materials support-
ing the right to die. Sponsors
conferences and workshops.

Hastings Center: Institute of Society, Ethics and the Life Sciences
360 Broadway
Hastings-on-Hudson, NY 10706
(914) 762-8500

Publishes bimonthly Hastings
Center Report, articles, book
reviews, and annual annotated
bibliographies, and holds
conferences on bio-medical
issues, including issues related
to death and dying.

National Hemlock Society
PO Box 11830
Eugene, OR 97440
(503) 342-5748

Information and support for
voluntary euthanasia (self-
deliverance) for terminally ill
adults and also for the
seriously, incurably physically
ill. Publishes books and other
informational materials to help
members decide the manner
and means of their death.
Quarterly newsletter to
members with up-to-date
information on issues of death

and dying. You can become a
member for a small fee ($15 or
$25 depending on your
circumstances).

FUNERAL PLANNING

National Funeral Directors Association
135 Wells Street
Milwaukee, WI 53202
(414) 541-2500

Leading trade association in the
funeral industry. Provides
literature, audiovisual materials
and speakers on many aspects
of bereavement and funeral
planning. Offers "after-care"
programs of grief counseling
after the funeral is over.

Neptune Society
1380 Lincoln Avenue
San Rafael, CA 94901
(415) 485-6830

Known for its ceremonial
scattering of ashes at sea,
Neptune Society is actually a
full-fledged mortuary. Memorial
societies like this provide a
wide range of low-cost options,
whether you desire cremation
or traditional funeral and
burial services. Look in your
Yellow Pages under *Cremation*
or *Funerals* to find similar
societies in your area.

HERE ARE SOME examples of the many books available which address the practical, legal and financial matters that come up whenever a death occurs. Included as well are books which also confront the harder emotional aspects of grief, loss and bereavement. Many of these might be found in the library of your local hospice, an excellent resource. After the funeral, when you are suddenly alone again with the loss, curling up with a book which confirms and validates your feelings and helps point the way to healing and getting back on your feet, can be a great comfort.

AGING

Extended Health Care at Home: A Complete and Practical Guide
Evelyn M. Baulch
Celestial Arts, Berkeley, CA, 1988

A resource for families facing long-term illnesses or injuries.

Starting with the first shock of diagnosis or accident, this book will guide you as you begin to deal with your changed life. How to find the right doctor (one who is sympathetic to your beliefs), assessing your choices, deciding which treatments to accept and which to decline, using community agencies for support. How to deal with pain, your attitude and the patient's attitude, emotions, and the possibility of death. Includes a Dying Person's Bill of Rights and a chapter on spirituality.

The Unfinished Business of Living: Helping Aging Parents Help Themselves
Elwood N. Chapman
Crisp Publications, Los Altos, CA, 1988

Directed to those in the middle generation who must deal with their children on one hand, and aging parents on the other.

A warm book which recognizes the family unit as the best source for coping with handicaps of the aging process. It is a book about relationships and communication with lots of exercises and examples of how to reduce the burden on all family members. Happiness is the goal of retirement, and this is a valuable guide to reasonable and sensitive support. Good list of support organizations.

Where Can Mom Live? A Family Guide to Living Arrangements for Elderly Parents
Vivian F. Carlin and Ruth Mansberg
Lexington Books, Lexington, MA, 1987

Using the words and experiences of real people, the authors point out the psychological, social, and financial consequences of all your options, providing families with the practical information they need to decide which alternative is right for them.

Discusses traditional housing options for the elderly as well as innovative concepts in shared and cooperative living. Besides moving in with grown children and nursing homes, the authors have researched the ideas of home or apartment sharing (staying put) with a housemate who will cook, clean, shop and drive; communal group homes of 5-15 people owned by a nonprofit group who provides housekeeping and other services; subsidized housing projects; adult communities; retirement towns and villages.

The appendix is an excellent resource for addresses of state commissions on aging, state associations of homes for the aging, state housing finance agencies, general resources and selected readings.

DEATH AND DYING

A Death of One's Own
Gerda Lerner
University of Wisconsin Press, Madison, WI, 1985

A piercing, personal account of a death in the family.

Chronicle by a wife of the eighteen months that followed her husband's diagnosis of a brain tumor. Full of the practical details of family life, and how drastically it is changed by the process of one member's dying. The author spares the reader no emotions, good or bad, noble or ignoble. The story she tells is straightforward and painful, but anyone who has been through, or is going through, anything similar will sympathize with the anguish as well as the bright possibilities for new understanding of what's important in life.

Caring for Your Own Dead
Lisa Carlson
Upper Access Publishers, Hinesburg, VT, 1987

Death is among the most intimate and personal of human events . . . By dealing with the physical aspects of death, emotional needs may be handled effectively as well.

A historical perspective on home funerals. With a state-by-state guide to present legal requirements, how to obtain and file permits, fill out a death certificate, listings of crematories that work directly with families, burial procedures, price variables. For those who want to take charge of their own burial arrangements, an invaluable, inspiring book.

Dealing Creatively with Death: A Manual of Death Education and Simple Burial
Ernest Morgan
Celo Press, Burnsville, NC, 1984

Confronting death enriches life.

An excellent little book. The death education part teaches how to relate to a dying person in a positive way, what you can expect from hospice care, ways of coping with bereavement, and tackles right-to-die issues such as your right to refuse treatment. Provides some ground rules for self-termination while speaking out against life-denying habits which account for self-destruction.

The simple burial part of the book makes suggestions for maintaining dignity and economy in funeral arrangements, what your options are for body disposal, financial resources at the time of a death and a checklist of things to be done. Provides guidance for those who decide not to use a funeral home, who wish to bury their own dead. Includes some lovely sample death ceremonies.

Death as a Fact of Life
David Hendin
W.W. Norton & Co., New York, NY, 1973

. . . brings together new information on death in fascinating and useful form, as medical journalist David Hendin deals with key moral and scientific issues.

A history of definitions of death, addressing the complex question: at what precise moment does death occur? The opposite end of "when does life begin?" which so puzzles abortion advocates and right-to-lifers. As medical technology has become advanced enough to keep someone alive artificially when the brain no longer functions, the question is raised daily, provoking profound debate in the legal, medical, science and ethics communities.

Other "taboo" subjects which the book faces are donation of body parts (at what moment is the donor dead enough to allow the transplant to occur yet still alive enough to contribute a useful organ?) Is euthanasia "good death" or murder? Under what conditions might it be appropriate? What about freezing people with the idea of bringing them back to life?

The book is practical, scientific and historical, rather than religious or philosophical, and raises some thought-provoking, relevant questions.

Meetings at the Edge:
Dialogues with the Grieving and the Dying, the Healing and the Healed
Stephen Levine
Anchor Books, Doubleday, New York, NY, 1984

This is a high-wire act. To keep the heart open in hell, to maintain some loving balance in the face of all our pain and confusion. To allow life in. To heal past our fear of the unknown.

Stephen Levine, together with his wife Ondrea, has written numerous books on dying, including *Who Dies?* Answer to the question: everyone. The author has made it his life's work to help make this powerful transition easier for others. A Buddhist, his work is infused with basic Buddhist precepts which call for acceptance and openness.

The dialogues are edited transcripts of phone calls with cancer patients, a husband of a dying wife, people who work with coma patients, a mother of a dying child, son of a dying father. They demonstrate the Levines' therapeutic process (or, as they call it, "spiritual counseling") in action. The conversations are warm, honest, and revelatory. The pain and suffering is never pushed away but breathed with, opened to, and let in, before it is allowed to pass through.

On Death and Dying
Elizabeth Kubler-Ross
Macmillan, New York, NY, 1969

Explores attitudes around the fear of dying.

Elizabeth Kubler-Ross is a renowned expert and has written many books on the subject of death. Here, she outlines the five stages of the dying process, which everyone goes through in one way or another, sometimes simultaneously, not necessarily in this order: denial and isolation, anger, bargaining, depression, and finally, hopefully, acceptance.

The Ruffian on the Stair: Reflections on Death
Rosemary Dinnage
Viking, New York, NY, 1990

We all know that we must die. . . How does the way in which we deal with this knowledge affect the quality of our lives?

Twenty-five interviews with people from varying backgrounds discussing their understanding of death. These people "talk frankly and bravely about their experience of bereavement, the value of 'dying well,' aspects of the one problem that is central to us all: how to bring meaning to our lives in the face of the fact that we are all going to die."

GRIEF AND HEALING

The First Year of Bereavement
Ira O. Glick, Robert S. Weiss, C. Murray Parkes
John Wiley & Sons, New York, NY, 1974

The forces of bereavement usually operate over a much longer time period that is more appropriately labeled a 'period of life transition' than a 'life crisis' . . . Many widows are still involved in an active psychosocial readjustment process during the second and third years of their bereavement.

A clinical analysis combining results of various studies of grieving widows. Some topics covered include: the availability and use of help, ceremonies of leave-taking, changes in relationships with family and friends, and patterns in the recovery process. The book is formal and analytical but reassuring in its conclusions: everyone reacts to grief differently. "In most cases, grief seems to resolve itself in time. Within three or four years . . . most had moved toward recovery, all of them different for having suffered the loss, but many of them stronger for having succeeded in going on."

A Gift of Hope: How We Survive Our Tragedies
Robert Veninga
Little, Brown and Company, Boston, MA, 1985

Why do some people survive a crisis when others give up?

Walks you through the stages of a crisis from shock to recovery. Told via interviews with people who have been through tragedy, the book offers survival strategies and suggests practical steps you can take: coping with initial panic and long-term anxiety, taking care of your physical health, how to recognize when you need help and where to find it.

The Grieving Time: A Year's Account of Recovery from Loss
Anne M. Brooks
The Dial Press, Garden City, NY, 1985

Beginning the journal as an answer to my need, I came to recognize its value as a therapeutic tool. Every time I wrote or reread it, there was the comfort of releasing sublimated grief.

A widow's journal, month by month, of how it feels to really grieve the death of the one you loved best, in the midst of friends, family and social obligations. Nice drawings.

Living Through Grief and Growing With It
Dr. Arthur Freese
Barnes & Noble Books, New York, NY, 1978

Provides the very information needed for one to lose one's fear of grief, to show how to grow with grief, how to find gain in the much more obvious loss.

What are the outer manifestations of inner grief? How long might it last? This gentle book answers these questions and suggests helpful mourning practices, avoiding mistakes in recovery and how others can help the bereaved. Addresses the grief that comes not only with death, but also with aging or retirement, childbirth, moving or surgery.

"Help comes from recognizing these normal human reactions that all of us undergo in highly individual degrees and widely varying combinations and forms during these most shaking and deepest human experiences."

Love, Medicine & Miracles: Lessons Learned About Self-Healing from a Surgeon's Experience with Exceptional Patients
Bernie S. Siegel, M.D.
Perennial Library, New York, NY, 1988

Our state of consciousness and disease are inseparable.

The famous book by surgeon Bernie Siegel is a testimony to his belief in the healing capabilities of the human mind. How to use positive attitude, imagery and a strong will to live in guiding the body along a healing path.

"Terms like spontaneous remission and miracle . . . imply that the patient must be lucky to be cured, but these healings occur through hard work . . . They happen by means of an inner energy available to all of us."

"If you are suffering from some life-threatening disease, the change I'm talking about may save your life or prolong it well past medical expectations. At the very least it will enable you to get more out of your remaining time than you think possible."

What Helped Me When My Loved One Died
ed. Earl A. Grollman
Beacon Press, Boston, MA, 1981

Modern society smothers the whole topic of death and bereavement in silence and embarrassment. The reality of grief is denied, and there are few outlets for pent-up anxieties, tensions, guilt feelings, anger, loneliness, loss of faith, and hopelessness about the future.

In human terms, spoken from the heart of experience, individuals and couples tell their own stories of shock, sadness, despair and recovery after the loss of a child, a spouse, a parent or friend, whether from illness, accident, suicide, or war. Many of the contributors have gone on to found important support groups, such as Compassionate Friends (for families of children who died), the SIDS Foundation (for victims of sudden infant death syndrome), Ronald McDonald House (for families of children with cancer), and Gold Star Mothers (whose sons have died in wars).

Towards the end of the book, physician William M. Lamers, Jr. writes this list of poems he has found useful:

Thanatopsis
William Cullen Bryant

The Dying Need But Little Dear
Emily Dickinson

Elegy Written in a Country Churchyard
Thomas Gray

Spring and Fall: To a Young Child
Gerard Manley Hopkins

To an Athlete Dying Young
A.E. Housman

Revisitation
Anne Morrow Lindbergh

Collected Sonnets
Edna St. Vincent Millay

With You a Part of Me Has Passed Away
George Santayana

When to the Sessions of Sweet Silent Thought
William Shakespeare

When Lilacs Last in the Dooryard Bloomed
Walt Whitman

Sailing to Byzantium
William Butler Yeats

SELF-DELIVERANCE AND EUTHANASIA

Easier Said Than Done: Moral Decisions in Medical Uncertainty
Milton D. Heifetz, M.D.
Prometheus Books, Buffalo, NY, 1992

Provocative.

A neurosurgeon describes the principles of an ethic that can help physicians, nurses, patients, and their families make the right medical decisions.

Euthanasia: The Moral Issues
ed. Robert M. Baird and Stuart M. Rosenbaum
Prometheus Books, Buffalo, NY, 1992

A valuable resource.

Brings together the views of moral theorists, physicians, advocates and opponents of euthanasia.

Final Exit: The Practicalities of Self-Deliverance and Assisted Suicide for the Dying
Derek Humphry
Hemlock Society, Eugene, OR, 1991

. . . intended to be read by a mature adult who is suffering from terminal illness and is considering the option of rational suicide if and when suffering becomes unbearable.

This book became an unexpected bestseller in 1991. The unusual and controversial parts of the book are its highly specific drug dosage tables. Practical information is offered on how to determine if self-deliverance is the best option. When to enlist the aid of doctors or nurses. How to deal with doctors and the law, insurance companies, autopsy. Using hospice as an alternative support system to alleviate physical and emotional pain. The pros and cons of using drugs, a plastic bag, or self-starvation.

Let Me Die Before I Wake: Hemlock's Book of Self-Deliverance for the Dying
Derek Humphry
The Hemlock Society, Eugene, OR, 1987

. . . describes not only painless ways to end one's life. It deals with the kinds of decisions someone facing such a prospect must make.

One of many Hemlock Society publications which support self-deliverance. Case studies of terminally ill individuals who made rational decisions to end their own lives, including the story of Humphry's wife Jean's death. The founding of the Hemlock Society, prescriptions for overdose, and a checklist of questions to ask before taking action.

Murder of Mercy: Euthanasia on Trial
Stanley M. Rosenblatt
Prometheus Books, Buffalo, NY, 1992

Demonstrates the hypocrisy and impotence of the medical and legal professions' attempts to grapple with euthanasia.

In 1987, Dr. Peter Rosier admitted on TV to helping his terminally ill wife commit suicide, then was indicted for murder and subsequently acquitted. Written by an attorney, explores controversial legal issues surrounding the proposed right to assist someone to die.

Prescription: Medicide
The Goodness of Planned Death
Jack Kevorkian, M.D.
Prometheus Books, Buffalo, NY, 1992.

Learn why 'suicide doctor' assists the terminally ill to die.

Explains Doctor Kevorkian's point of view regarding medical reforms necessary to create a rational — and legal — program of dignified, humane and beneficial planned death. See *Right to Die*, page 95, for more on physician assisted aid-in-dying.

WILLS AND FINANCES

Answers
Becky Barker
Corpus Christi, TX, 1981

When Becky Barker became a widow unexpectedly, she was faced with decisions and questions she was not adequately prepared to answer.

The book she compiled to help others through the muddle of paperwork following a death is a 3-ring binder with tabbed sections and pockets for storing copies of important documents. Forms are to be filled in now, listing information on finances, properties, insurance and business matters.

How to Avoid Probate — Updated!
Norman F. Dacey
Crown Publishers, New York, NY, 1987

A do-it-yourself guide to probate avoidance.

A big, fat bestselling book which provides detailed legal advice and detachable forms designed to help assets go directly to heirs without the time, expense and publicity of going through probate. Suggests devices which permit settlement of estates with little or no court involvement and minimal involvement of lawyers. Procedures for transferring property without administration.

Set Your House in Order:
A Practical Way to Prepare for Death
Miles O'Brien Riley.
Doubleday & Company, Garden City, NY, 1980

A broad and basic workbook for death preparation.

Written by a priest, includes forms to fill in on financial and other matters. Practical, religious and anecdotal.

Simple Will Book: How to Prepare
A Legally Valid Will
Denis Clifford
Nolo Press, Berkeley, CA, 1991

A book that allows most adult Americans to safely and privately prepare a valid will.

A clear, nicely presented guide through the jumble of laws about making a valid will, including ownership laws, providing for children, and sample basic will forms.

Survival Kit for Wives: How to Avoid
Financial Chaos When Tragedy Strikes
Don and Renee Martin
Villard Books, New York, NY, 1986

Does for the family what One-Minute Manager *did for executives.*

A workbook to help you get your family records and documents in order, to assist in meeting your current needs and be prepared should tragedy strike. Advice on credit, budgeting, protecting assets, insurance, providing for children, the job market, and emotional recovery. First half of book is text with advice, second half is worksheets to be filled in. Also contains a detailed suggested reading list and sources for more information.

Who Gets It When You Go? A Guide for
Planning Your Will, Protecting Your Family's
Financial Future, Minimizing Inheritance
Taxes, and Avoiding Probate
David C. Larsen
Random House, New York, NY, 1982

Explains in uncomplicated language what can happen to your property when you die.

Introduction to a complex subject. The title tells it all.

Widows in the Dark: Rescuing Your Financial Position
Elizabeth Smith Gatov
Common Knowledge Press, Bolinas, CA, 1985

Achieve a rewarding sense of financial independence through a grasp of the fundamentals of investing.

Advice to any woman suddenly taking on "the burden of financial management that had always been her husband's responsibility . . . at a time of enormous emotional stress."

WillMaker 4.0, *software*
Legisoft, Inc.
Nolo Press, Berkeley, CA, 1992

An easy-to-use and inexpensive program with an excellent manual that explains the legal complications of making a will.

You can make a computer-generated will adapted to your particular situation, using the legal and practical information available in this software program for the home PC (IBM or Mac). How to provide for heirs, name a guardian for minor children, create a children's trust or leave property to children using a new law, the Uniform Transfers to Minors Act. Contains two different property management systems. "WillMaker can educate you about which option is best suited to your needs." For people with simple wills, demonstrates easy procedures to follow.

You and Your Will: The Planning and Management of Your Estate
Paul P. Ashley
New American Library, New York, NY, 1985

Prepares the client to make maximum and economical use of an attorney.

A pocket-sized paperback with a state-by-state breakdown of laws regulating wills. Furnishes the background necessary for the writing of a wiser will. Suggestions for "stretching the dollars," choosing beneficiaries, trusts, avoiding taxes, providing for children. Not a do-it-yourself manual.

INDEX

ABOUT THE AUTHOR

ELMO A. PETTERLE was a personnel manager in the North Bay division for Pacific Gas and Electric Company in California for 25 years. His responsibilities included hiring, employee benefits, salary administration, and industrial relations. Part of his job involved making the initial contact with survivors when an employee died. In most of these cases, the survivor — in addition to grief and sorrow — had to cope with the many legal, financial and other complexities that a death entails. This firsthand experience led Elmo to the realization that most people are not prepared, emotionally or otherwise, to handle the suddenly-inherited responsibilities that accompany the death of a loved one.

When Elmo retired in 1979, he decided to put his own house in order. After accomplishing this, he decided to help others by creating a practical workbook that could be filled out while one is in good health and of sound mind. *Legacy of Love* was originally self-published in 1983, then revised and published by Shelter Publications in 1986. Over 15,000 copies were sold. *Getting Your Affairs in Order* is an updated, more concise edition of *Legacy of Love.*

Elmo and his wife Kay live in San Rafael, California. They are both avid golfers and live 300 feet from the first tee of a golf course. They have three children and eight grandchildren.

ABOUT THE EDITORS

ROBERT C. KAHN worked as an insurance broker for 30 years. His expertise on insurance, investments, financial and other business matters was invaluable in the creation of most of the forms that appear in the book.

MARIANNE ROGOFF has been an editor since 1983 for numerous Shelter Publications projects, including *Legacy of Love.* For this book, she reorganized and updated the text and contributed research and writing on new right-to-die laws, support groups and books.

CREDITS

Publisher: Lloyd Kahn

Designer: David Wills

Production Manager: Marianne Rogoff

Production: Christina Reski

Cover Design: Suzanne Hathcock

Marbled Paper: Doris Allen

Special thanks
Joan Creed
Executive Assistant
Shelter Publications

George Young
Hal Hershey
Ten Speed Press

Bruce Stilson
Attorney

Michael White
Californians Against Human Suffering

Sue Buster
Hospice of Marin

Stephen Jamison, Ph.D.
Hemlock Society

Text Paper: 60 lb. Glatfelter

Software: Quark Express 3.1

Printers: Courier Companies, Inc., Westford, MA

Did you know that 93% of all families are unprepared when a death occurs?

GETTING YOUR AFFAIRS IN ORDER solves this problem.

GETTING YOUR AFFAIRS IN ORDER is easy to use. By filling in clear, simple forms, you can leave your eventual survivors a record — all in one place — of:

- Cemetery, mortuary and memorial service arrangements
- Relatives, close friends and business associates to contact
- Benefits survivors are entitled to, including:

  - Life insurance
  - Pensions, IRA, Keogh plans
  - Social Security
  - Medicare and medical insurance

GETTING YOUR AFFAIRS IN ORDER also provides:

- A priority list of what to do in the first hours, days and months after a death
- Information on finances, investments, wills, probate and right to die
- Sources for grief support, hospice aid and books

GETTING YOUR AFFAIRS IN ORDER is a true gift for those you will one day leave behind.

If you feel this book and the information included is worthwhile and might be useful to others, photocopy this page and send it to a friend, relative or neighbor. Or if you would like us to notify anyone about GETTING YOUR AFFAIRS IN ORDER, please send us their name and address and we'll be glad to send our catalog with mail-order information.

PURCHASING ADDITIONAL COPIES: To purchase additional copies of GETTING YOUR AFFAIRS IN ORDER, check your local bookstore or fill out the order form below. If you would like us to mail copies to others, please indicate.

DISCOUNTS are available for books used as premiums or for promotional purposes. Contact our distributor, Ten Speed Press, Special Sales (510–841–2665).

GETTING YOUR AFFAIRS IN ORDER
by Elmo A. Petterle

$12.95 plus $3.00 shipping and handling first book, $1.00 each additional book

Send to:

SHELTER PUBLICATIONS
P.O. Box 279
Bolinas, CA 94924

NAME _____

ADDRESS _____

CITY _____

STATE _____ ZIP _____